'I can make th[...]
hold you,' Tan[...]

'Can you?' There[...]
softening to Jason Tysak's tone and his eyes
bored into hers until she had to fight not to look
away. 'If you can get the better of me, Miss
Rawson, you surely would deserve a big
reward. I'll have to see what I can come up
with.'

Dear Reader

Autumn's here and the nights are drawing in—but when better to settle down with your favourite romances? This month, Mills & Boon have made sure that you won't notice the colder weather—our wide range of love stories are sure to warm the chilliest of hearts! Whether you're wanting a rattling good read, something sweet and magical, or to be carried off to hot, sunny countries—like Australia, Greece or Venezuela—we've got the books to please you.

Enjoy!

The Editor

Patricia Wilson was born in Yorkshire and lived there until she married and had four children. She loves travelling and has lived in Singapore, Africa and Spain. She had always wanted to be a writer but a growing family and career as a teacher left her with little time to pursue her interest. With the encouragement of her family she gave up teaching in order to concentrate on writing and her other interests of music and painting.

Recent titles by the same author:

WALK UPON THE WIND
OUT OF NOWHERE
DARK ILLUSION

RECKLESS
CRUSADE

BY

PATRICIA WILSON

MILLS & BOON LIMITED
ETON HOUSE   18-24 PARADISE ROAD
RICHMOND   SURREY   TW9 1SR

*First published in Great Britain 1992
by Mills & Boon Limited*

© Patricia Wilson 1992

*Australian copyright 1992
Philippine copyright 1992
This edition 1992*

ISBN 0 263 77793 6

*Set in Times Roman 10 on 12 pt.
01-9211-54080 C*

Made and printed in Great Britain

CHAPTER ONE

Just for one moment, as she parked the car and looked across to the shop, Tamara Rawson forgot the great impediment, the major snag, the fly in the ointment, and then her tawny eyes moved slowly along the lovely old buildings in Lancrest Mews and rested irritably on the great hoarding that stood like an alien against the old hotel at the end. 'Tysak Holdings.' Boldly, brashly and arrogantly it blazoned its message—'Danger. Reconstruction Work.'

Tamara's lips tightened angrily and all pleasure fled. That infuriating message was the first thing she saw every day as she arrived to open her exclusive shop, and, even after a buying trip to London, there it was again, reminding her of her daily problem. The reconstruction work was severely interfering with her business and she had dark suspicions about the future plans of the owner of that hated name.

Jason Tysak! She hadn't even met him, but she knew his name as well as she knew her own, and small wonder—wasn't it pushed down her throat daily along with the dust, noise and general upheaval? She slammed the car door and marched across the small park to the mews. She had chosen this place very carefully when she had decided to sink all her capital into Impressions.

It was not a shop really, it was a salon, a chic and elegant centre of fashion that catered for the rich matrons of the town and their clothes-conscious daughters. Now they were beginning to complain, not about the

lovely clothes on view, not about the well-informed and
courteous service, but about the dust, the noise and the
lowering of the tone of the place. It was rocking Tamara's
boat and she fumed daily. There wasn't a thing she could
do about it.

Almost every penny she possessed was wrapped up in
Impressions, and things had been going swimmingly until
that hoarding had appeared one morning, to be followed very rapidly by tough-looking workmen who
hammered, sawed, demolished and sang at the top of
their voices to a small but efficient transistor radio. They
were very cheerful men but exceedingly boisterous.

A polite request from Eric Simpson at the hairdressing salon had gained cheeky grins and the lowering
of the music by one decibel. Apparently they had no
authority over their voices and a hammer had a mind
of its own. Dust was uncontrollable and decided its
course after consultation with the breeze. Eric Simpson
had this fact straight from the foreman, and over the
few weeks Tamara's temper was becoming uncontrollable too.

She had written letters of complaint, threatened legal
action, but nothing had been forthcoming except polite
regrets and promises of a speedy end to the torture.
Nothing was happening speedily. The men were having
their lunch and they had the cheek to wave to her from
their perches high up on the scaffolding. The transistor
radio was playing rock music. She glared up at them and
they grinned back merrily.

The door was locked and Tamara looked impatiently
at her watch before realising that it was Janet's lunch
break. She let herself in and she could see straight away
that there was dust in here. No matter how careful they
were, it seeped in. Even though she had only gone out

for half an hour, Janet had thrown plastic covers over
the racks of clothes, and Tamara left them there.

She walked to the window and looked out towards the
road, fighting down an urge to storm along to the hotel
and shout at somebody. It would do no good; the men
were just builders, and none of this was their fault. Jason
Tysak was one of those people who moved around with
great plans, altering traditional things and consulting
nobody at all. He had temporary offices in Victoria
Crescent at the other end of the town; one of the old
houses had been vacant and he had slid himself neatly
in between solicitors, land agents and doctors. The whole
crescent was now rather select business premises and
there he was—camouflaged.

Tamara stared grimly through the window. The place
they rather lovingly called the park was actually just a
strip of land that stretched from the road to the cobbled
path that fronted the four shops. Wrought-iron railings
kept it apart from the road, a few flowering bushes
brightened it and a little gate allowed access to the path.
It wasn't much wider than the lawn to a good-sized house
but it was long and edged by beech trees.

There was an Edwardian elegance to Lancrest Mews.
It was a little jewel in a busy town, and its tranquillity
drew the wealthy clientele and their aspiring daughters.
Impressions was now a well-known place for beautiful
clothes, Tamara's own creation. She had been a model
since she was sixteen and when at almost twenty-four
she had received a legacy she had risked everything to
start here. With her own flair and the contacts she had
in London from her modelling days, she was able to do
her own buying and satisfy a need that had made the
business pay well.

There were four shops in Lancrest Mews. Eric Simpson had a stylish hairdressing salon at the very end, closest to the hotel. Next door was Edwina Brown with a shop selling lingerie, swimwear, good costume jewellery, silk scarves and accessories. Tamara often bought for Edwina in London. At the other side Kenneth Dennison had a shoe shop—Italian shoes and bags—and together they collected all the good trade, a quartet of fashion and taste, a haven for the discerning with only the park to cross after they had parked their cars. Everything had been rosy until Jason Tysak had exploded on to the scene.

They had simply heard that someone had bought the Old Manor Hotel that stood high and slightly derelict at the end of the mews. None of them had been prepared for the sight of walls being demolished, old doors being ripped out and sections of roof disappearing. At first they had imagined it was to be pulled down, some monstrosity taking its place, but no such thing. It was being extended and altered, and Tamara had dark suspicions as to where it would eventually extend itself to— the whole of the mews!

Jason Tysak owned land and property all over the country—all over the world, in fact—so naturally they had never seen him. He certainly would not be sitting quietly in the offices on Victoria Crescent. He would not be loafing around the hotel to oversee the work either. He would just issue orders. So far he had simply ignored the discreet shops in Lancrest Mews as if he were sublimely unaware of their existence, but Tamara was not fooled. He wanted them. She was sure he did. Every instinct told her that.

Tamara walked to the small office at the back of the shop and started sorting out the mail. She had been away for three days and it was astonishing how things piled up. She caught sight of herself in the mirror above her small writing desk and grimaced at her own tight expression. Much more of Jason Tysak and she would be drawn and wrinkled by the time she was twenty-five, and that was only a few weeks away.

The sun slanted in at the window, catching all the fire of her hair, a honey-gold that was almost red. It was shoulder-length and very wavy, but now it was caught in a loose knot at the back of her head, drawn from her face to reveal the fine bone-structure and wide amber eyes that had been such an asset in her modelling career. She relaxed her face slowly, feeling her tight shoulder muscles ease too, making her beautiful mouth smile. He might be wrecking her business but he was not going to turn her into a bitter, angry shrew. Quietly and methodically she would deal with Jason Tysak because she had the feeling that it would be left to her to do something about him.

Her frame of mind restored to peace, Tamara turned with a smile as the door opened and her assistant stepped into the shop. Janet Piper had been with her since the start of this venture and Tamara always felt quite happy about leaving the business in her hands when she had to be away in London.

'I'm back.' Her cheerful greeting failed to bring an answering smile, and Tamara felt the first quiverings of alarm.

'Yes. I noticed your car. Did you order anything spectacular?'

If she hadn't known better Tamara would have fancied that Janet was avoiding her eyes. The uneasy feeling grew, but she determinedly pushed it aside.

'A few special things. It just about completes our spring collection, and spring is almost upon us,' Tamara pointed out, keeping deliberately jaunty. 'The snow-drops are out, I see.'

'Yes. Crocuses coming through a bit.'

It was more than Tamara could stand. Her enforced calm deserted her.

'Janet, what is it? I know something's wrong, so no hedging.'

Janet took off her coat in what appeared to be a deliberately protracted way, and Tamara's tension increased.

'Janet!'

'Oh, heavens! I thought I wouldn't dare tell you and now I'm sure.' Janet looked at her friend and employer anxiously. She knew the formidable temper. 'Jason Tysak bought Lancrest Mews,' she said in a little desperate rush, wishing someone else could have broken the news. Tamara was a bit obsessed by Jason Tysak. She had not lived well with the upheaval, and now she looked almost threatening.

'How do you know?' Tamara regarded Janet coolly, and Janet knew that the 'cold eye' was not for her at all; it merely promised trouble to come.

'Eric Simpson told me this morning. He and Edwina have both had letters from the Tysak solicitors. I expect you'll get one tomorrow. I—I mean, the post...'

'I expect so.' Tamara walked back to the window and returned to her staring across the park. So it had finally come! All her suspicions had been correct. Their leases were just about ready for renewing but now they would not be renewed at all because they would have a new landlord, one who intended to pull down Lancrest Mews and extend that hotel over the whole area. It was the end of Impressions, and no amount of hoping would change facts. The fact that she had subconsciously been expecting it made it all the more devastating.

She just walked out of the door and went in to see Edwina, and the whole thing began again.

'Oh, you're back! Get anything special?'

'I've been through this once with Janet,' Tamara snapped. 'How can you be even interested, Edwina? What about the leases?'

'Well, Tysak bought the whole works, darling.' Edwina Brown was comfortably and elegantly middle-aged, well made up and perfumed, and she smiled wryly at Tamara's furious looks. 'It's absolutely useless to get into a rage, Tamara. There's a lot of small print. The property can be sold at any time, providing the buyer offers reasonable compensation if he intends to turn us out. As we're almost at the end of our leases anyway, the compensation would be negligible. However, I've been on to the offices of Tysak Holdings and they assure me that there is no intention to turn us out permanently.'

'Permanently?' Tamara's golden eyes narrowed with suspicion.

'Well,' Edwina perched on the edge of a tall, upholstered stool, 'apparently, there'll be a bit of upheaval. We're getting a face-lift.'

'What do you mean, a face-lift?' Tamara glared and fumed more at Edwina's calm smile.

'We have to move out for a few weeks at the end of this month while they sand-blast the fronts of the shops, bring them into line with the new look of the Old Manor Hotel. Then we move back and everything goes on as normal—with a new landlord.'

'You believe all this? You actually believe that man will let us come back here?' Tamara demanded. 'Once out, we're out for good, I can tell you. When, for example, do we sign the new leases?'

'As far as we can tell, when we move back in, because, you see,' Edwina added hurriedly when Tamara looked explosive, 'we move out on the day our leases expire and then we won't even be here for weeks. It was explained to both Kenneth and myself when we went down to the offices. In our temporary accommodation we'll be paying more rent than we do here, and we don't want to take on two things at once, now, do we?'

How could anyone be so naïve? Tamara looked at her in disbelief and went round to the shoe shop to see Kenneth Dennison. He believed it too, and so did Eric when she stormed into the perfumed interior of his hairdressing salon. How could they be so blind? It was as clear as glass. Jason Tysak was about to give them the order of the boot and he wasn't even honest enough to send them letters telling them to quit. No wonder he was a millionaire—some old goat with glassy eyes and a smarmy smile, no doubt.

With lunchtime over, business got under way again, but Tamara had to force a smile to her face. The great problem was uppermost in her mind.

'Have you fixed a date for the fashion show, Tamara?' One of the town's most wealthy matrons called in and stopped to ask about the show that Impressions organised each year.

'Yes, Mrs Prost. The same venue as usual too. One or two models are coming up from London, and then the local girls, of course.' She added that last hastily as Mrs Prost's eyes slightly glazed over. The beloved daughter always modelled for Tamara; she was tall, pretty and quite unreliable, but it would not be at all wise to overlook her, not if she wished to keep the business of Mrs Prost and friends.

'So when is it going to be?' The smiles were back, and Tamara consulted her notes.

'March twenty-seventh, at seven sharp. All the new stock will be in by then.'

It wasn't until the door closed behind this very satisfied customer that the date rang a bell with Tamara. The twenty-seventh! That was exactly four days before the leases ran out. There was always a rush of buying after the yearly show, and this time they would be knee-deep in packing to move out. She walked through to the back of the shop, thinking furiously. What could she do to outwit this man? He seemed to have them neatly tied up.

After a casual glance out of the back window she was back again very speedily.

'Janet! Who are those men hanging around behind the shops?' she asked anxiously, already knowing deep down who they were.

'Oh, there's an architect from Tysak Holdings and two surveyors from the construction firm and a man who was here yesterday from the county council. I did check up on them when they first came,' Janet added in a pleased voice, well content with her efficiency. 'They had credentials. They came into the shop too. They wanted to see the back area.'

'Why?' Tamara held her breath, but she was no wiser after the answer.

'I don't know. They didn't say. But they were very nice.'

No doubt! They would have had their orders. So this was it. Her suspicions were confirmed: Jason Tysak had every intention of swallowing Lancrest Mews and adding it to the hotel. Well, she would go down fighting, all flags flying, and she would tear away his façade of respectability at the same time. It was not something to be put off. Action was required and it was required right now.

'Lock up if I'm not back at five-thirty, Janet,' she muttered, and then she collected her things and went.

The offices in Victoria Crescent were well lit up, because there were so many tall old trees along the road that light hardly ever penetrated the rooms. Tamara knew that for sure because her dentist had rooms along this road. Tysak Holdings didn't have rooms, though; they had the whole of number sixty-three, the biggest house on the road, and Tamara pulled up outside and marched across to storm the ramparts. Just let them tell her she had no appointment! She didn't want to see the great Tysak personally—he was probably sunning himself in the West Indies, his nurse handing out medicine. All she wanted was to state her case and send him a message of defiance—for now. The rest she would work out in secret.

She had to get past the quite young girl at the reception desk first, and that proved to be very easy when she mentioned Lancrest Mews. It gave her entry to higher things—Mr Tysak's personal assistant. So he had left his Man Friday here to face the bullets? Tamara walked up the expensively carpeted stairs and prepared to face stiffer opposition.

Man Friday was a well-groomed brunette of about thirty-three, and Tamara eyed her clothes appreciatively. Well paid, she speculated, knowing good clothes when she saw them, or 'well kept', her mind added spitefully. She was a bit ashamed of that when the brunette smiled warmly and came forward.

'You're very lucky, Miss Rawson,' she said pleasantly. 'Mr Tysak is here at the moment.'

'Himself?' Tamara asked idiotically, quite taken aback. How would his poor old chest be standing up to an English winter?

'Oh, yes. We don't often have the pleasure,' the disciple sighed. 'He's been here for two days and he'll see you.' Her expression said that he was very kind to consider small mortals, however beautifully dressed. Her eyes ran over Tamara's dark gold suit, the short jacket lined with white fake fur, the matching boots of pale leather. The whole made a picture of tawny elegance, the amber eyes glowing in a beautiful face. Miss Phillips made a note to visit Impressions and led the way to the inner sanctum.

'Miss Rawson,' she breathed and then simply melted away, closing the door with no sound at all, and Tamara was left standing in a high-ceilinged comfortable room all alone. There was a huge desk by the window and a very high-backed leather chair turned to face outside. Apart from several extremely expensive-looking pieces of antique furniture and a few impressive pictures there was nothing else, certainly no wily old man.

Where on earth was he? Under the desk? Had he collapsed? Tamara stood there, wide-eyed and intrigued, her anger slowly draining away at this unexpected turn of events. It looked as if there was no dragon to face. And then as the chair slowly swung round she found that the room was not at all empty. Jason Tysak had not collapsed, and her mental pictures of a decrepit miser faded away as she found herself being regarded steadily by dark, intent eyes.

'Please sit down, Miss Rawson.' He stood politely and motioned her to a seat facing him across the wide expanse of the desk, and she could see at once that he would be a formidable foe. There was something about him that made a wave of confusion race over her. Without anything more than his polite invitation to sit he had stilled her ready tongue.

Six feet two in his socks, she thought dazedly. He was handsome, aesthetically handsome, not one ounce of spare flesh on him at first glance. His cheekbones were high, classical, his eyes dark and spiked with black lashes that matched the dark, beautifully groomed hair—it tried to curl but didn't quite dare, she noted. He was deeply tanned and even the way he stood proclaimed a physical strength and co-ordination that was as natural as his air of power. In spite of the dark grey suit and pristine white shirt with silk tie, he looked dangerous, dramatically so; a noble savage.

'Geronimo,' she whispered thoughtlessly and the dark brows rose in astonishment, an expression of near-amusement and some other indefinable feeling flickering for a moment in his dark eyes.

'I beg your pardon?'

'You surprised me,' Tamara muttered, her cheeks beginning to glow a little at her own idiotic behaviour. This was not a good way to start a battle to the death.

'I apologise. I was studying the street. A very beautiful crescent.'

He was probably wondering how many hotels he could shove into it. The suspicion brought Tamara back to earth with a bang and she sat facing him when he motioned her to the seat again.

'What can I do for you, Miss Rawson?' She didn't trust those gleaming eyes for one second. He couldn't be more than in his thirties, so how was it that he already owned millions? It had to be by sharp practices because *she* would never be a millionaire even if she lived to be a hundred and sixty, and everyone had told her gloomily that she was starting a business when she was too young. Her amber eyes sharpened at his tone, commanding, polite but almost bored. It made her cheeks flush with annoyance, most of it with herself. She had come here to state her case and threaten action, not to stare mesmerised at the enemy.

'You could leave the town but I don't imagine it would help much, the damage already having been done,' she said, deliberately cold.

'Your complaints have been passed on to me,' he assured her, apparently discounting her icy looks and sarcastic comments. 'If any of your—merchandise has been damaged then of course the company will replace it or recompense you. We have no wish to cause discomfort to any of the present tenants of Lancrest Mews.'

Present tenants! Tamara's mind snapped on to that phrase, fastened on it like the teeth of a terrier. They wouldn't be there for long, by the sound of it.

'It is not merchandise!' Tamara said hotly. 'It's impossible to buy clothes like ours anywhere in this part of the country. Impressions is a very exclusive salon.'

'Possibly,' he agreed, 'for this town. I understand you have dust?' he added, glancing at the papers on his desk which even from here she could see were her own complaints. His observation made her feel as if she had been in close contact with the inside of a vacuum cleaner and caught something nasty, and Tamara's temper rose higher.

'There is dust, grit, noise and a general lowering of the tone of Lancrest Mews!' she bit out. 'The mews shops are very special, Mr Tysak.'

'Yes.' His dark eyes were on her furious face and tossing tawny-gold curls. On the way here they had escaped from the loose knot and she had forgotten to re-fasten them. His glance ran over the shining glory of them. 'Yes, special altogether. That's why I bought them. They need a fair bit of work doing, but it will be worthwhile.'

'For whom? I know perfectly well you intend to allow that monstrosity to encroach on Lancrest Mews.'

'Monstrosity? You mean the hotel? Have you seen the plans, Miss Rawson?'

'I have, but I don't believe it for a moment. I know what you're going to do. You're going to keep the façade, the shops too, and you're going to move sneakily behind and expand until the hotel takes up the whole of the mews. In all probability the fronts of the mews shops will end up as the windows of some hideous lounge in the hotel, all draped in glowing pink.'

'You're no architect, Miss Rawson, I can see that quite plainly.' He suddenly sounded amused, condescendingly amused. 'Let me explain it to you.' He stood smoothly, but Tamara too was on her feet. She was not about to accept any patronising attitude. Since she had stormed in here he had come close to making her feel foolishly vulnerable. If he got away with things normally by flaunting his powerful masculinity he was up against stiffer opposition this time.

'Don't bother, because I wouldn't believe a word you said. I intend to expose you, so get ready for action.'

'If it amuses you, Miss Rawson,' he agreed politely, and it infuriated her to see the way his lips twitched with sardonic amusement. Money could do anything, his dark eyes seemed to be saying, but Tamara thought not.

People power was greater. Perhaps he had never met people power before?

'It does not amuse me, Mr Tysak! However, I can promise to lessen *your* amusement. It's the beginning of March and the leases run to the end of March. That gives me plenty of time to act. I'm not quite as ready as the others to move at your command. I intend to fight this.'

'I own the property, Miss Rawson, and I have planning permission.'

'And that wasn't obtained in a day either,' Tamara fumed. 'No doubt you intend to put in new plans when we've all been evicted. Well, you won't get them through. I'll see to it.'

'I'm an irresistible force,' he assured her coldly, not entirely amused now, and she glared at him with furious amber eyes.

'And I am an immovable object. Just try to dislodge me! There's nothing you can do to stop me either because until the end of March we're quite safe.'

'I'm not sure that a girl like you can bank on safety.' His glance ran over her very comprehensively, deliberately insolent, a very male speculation in his eyes. She had the shocking feeling that he was slowly undressing her, and then he pressed a button on his desk and the door opened soundlessly as his assistant stood at adoring attention.

'Show Miss Rawson out, Miss Phillips,' he murmured, 'and give her a copy of the plans for Lancrest Mews.' He sounded utterly bored, dismissive, and after his chauvinistic appraisal it shocked her into a feeling of being found wanting as a female.

'No, thank you! They're carved across my heart!' Tamara marched out, infuriated that he had got under her skin with the oldest trick in the book. She was infuriated further when just before the door swished shut she heard low dark laughter. He thought he held all the cards. Power, wealth and sexual superiority. He would find out. 'He who laughs last laughs longest,' she muttered as she got into her car and drove away. They had all better be prepared, everybody on Victoria Crescent too, because he wasn't the sort of man who sat contemplating something for no reason at all. The beautiful crescent was beautiful to him because it spelled money, development money. Plunderer! There was nothing noble about that particular savage.

It was too late to go back to the shop and she went straight home to her flat. The money she had not used on the shop she had used on this flat. She owned it and she felt soothed as soon as she closed the door behind her. It was the entire ground floor of a large Victorian house at the edge of town, and she had done all the interior designing herself. She had made no attempt to go for a period effect. Everything was pastel shades, from walls to carpets to the oatmeal-coloured suite. The colour came in curtains, cushions and the bright good prints that decorated the walls. The huge one over the fireplace had been a present from her agent when she had taken the plunge and started her business. It was a glowing print of London with St Paul's in the background and, looking at it now, she wished herself back there.

Quick-tempered or not, she had no wish to fight anyone. Scenes were not her style and neither was battle, but she hated injustice and she had been taught to stand on her own two feet and face things squarely. She made herself a cup of tea and then settled down to the telephone, kicking off her boots and taking off her suit jacket before snuggling into the soft cushions and turning for solace to a place where it always rested.

'Hello, Mum? I'm back.' She found herself smiling as soon as she heard her mother's voice.

'Did you buy anything special, darling?'

This time it did nothing to annoy. She spent a few blissful minutes sharing her London trip with her mother, imagining her mother's kind, pretty face and feeling she were back at home, where trouble never reared its ugly head.

'Where's Dad?' Tamara asked when Susan Rawson had been duly appreciative of the descriptions of this season's spring stock.

'Out, Tamara. Where else? He has his rounds to do before evening surgery. Do you know we've still got snow up here? It's lingering quite unforgivably and making Jeffrey's job so much harder. The house calls take such a lot longer at this time of the year, apart from the bouts of flu and sprained ankles.'

Tamara knew. Her father was a doctor in a Cumbrian village that was beautiful in late spring and summer but where driving conditions were extremely hazardous at this time of the year. She wished she were home now. She wanted to tell them both about Jason Tysak, to see her father's greying head nod in agreement at what she had decided to do, to see her mother's outrage at high-handed ways. It was no use; she didn't have the time to drive up there. There was the fashion show to organise, and then of course there was a war to start.

As soon as she put the phone down it rang, and it was Roger Hart, editor of the local paper and her part-time boyfriend.

'Hello! You're back, then?'

'If you ask if I bought anything special I'll scream,' Tamara warned laughingly.

'Just so that you're back, love. My fashion editor will ask about clothes. I can do you a full-page ad at a very good rate,' he offered breezily, 'but first, have dinner with me tonight.'

'I'd love to,' Tamara assured him quickly, back into battle mode. 'I've got a lot to say.'

'Yes can be said with little time taken,' he murmured seductively. 'I'll pick you up at seven-thirty.'

He rang off then, and Tamara sat looking at the phone ruefully. It was Roger who called himself her part-time boyfriend and, although he said it laughingly, it worried her sometimes. He was just a friend, a good one but still nothing more than that. Modelling in London had taught her to watch her step, and maybe she watched it a little too carefully, but she was not and never would be interested in casual affairs. It would be love or nothing, and, much as she liked him, she did not love Roger.

Even so, she was always pleased to see him and this evening more so than ever. She trusted him completely and as they settled down to their meal in a quiet local restaurant she leaned forward and prepared to enlighten him about her plans and gain whatever aid she could.

'You know about the fate of Lancrest Mews, I suppose?'

'What fate?' He was instantly alert, all editor and newsman, and Tamara knew she had his full attention.

'In my opinion, Jason Tysak is about to incorporate the whole of the mews into the Old Manor Hotel.'

'Not possible.' Roger shook his fair head and got on with his meal, relieved to know that nothing had escaped his eagle eye. 'I've seen the plans. They're there at the council offices for all to see. We printed the planning request and the permission. Nobody objected.'

'Of course they didn't!' Tamara said indignantly. 'Who would object to the Old Manor Hotel being restored? The place was an eyesore.'

'Well, you've objected daily since work began,' Roger stated with an amused glance at her. 'So have your customers in their refined way. I've never had so many "Letters to the Editor". We had to allocate more space two weeks ago.'

'I object to the uncouth way they're going about it. There's nothing discreet. No tarpaulins and things like that, just noise, dirt and dust. But that's beside the point. Annoying as it is, one day it will be finished. Now, however, Jason Tysak is going to extend it along the whole of Lancrest Mews.'

'He can't, love,' Roger explained patiently. 'There's an order on those places. They're a true Edwardian façade.'

'But what about the backs?' Tamara asked triumphantly. 'What about the tatty bits and pieces that have been added over the years before planning permission ruled? There's a big area behind the shops. Suppose, just suppose, that the façades were kept and cleaned up nicely, add to it even the front rooms. Once you step into the back rooms and the backs of the buildings you've got a medley of indiscriminate additions.'

'I agree. But what's your point?' Roger cradled his wine glass and watched her intently. He wanted to laugh but he knew better. She looked like a beautiful foreign agent planning her assignment.

'If I were Jason Tysak,' Tamara continued darkly, 'if I had untold wealth and no scruples I would keep the façade of Lancrest Mews. I would sweep the Old Manor

Hotel into an extension around the back of the mews. I would call it Lancrest Mews Hotel, Edwardian elegance for the discerning. I would boot out the present tenants and have the park as a very nice frontage to the hotel.'

'A deadly plan,' Roger agreed, nodding sagely. 'However, nothing like that is in the wind.'

'Then I'll give you some news,' Tamara offered triumphantly. 'Jason Tysak has bought Lancrest Mews. We all move out at the end of March, supposedly for a brief time until the fronts are sand-blasted. No date has been set for the renewal of the leases, and over the past two days men have been round the back of the mews, examining and measuring. They were architects, surveyors and a man from the county council, probably the planning officer. Now what about the deadly plan?'

Roger put down his knife and fork and regarded her intently. She could see the look of the hunting newshound. She had him hooked. If there was anything to find out, Roger would find it. Score one for the little people!

CHAPTER TWO

ROGER arrived at the shop next day just after eleven, and Tamara knew he was hunting news as soon as she saw him. The architect was round at the back with the other men, and after a brief inspection through the window Roger sauntered out of the back door and began an easygoing conversation. Tamara watched as often as customers allowed, her excitement growing the longer Roger stayed. She would know for sure after this.

'Well? What did you find out?' She pounced on him as he came back in looking very thoughtful, but he shook his head.

'Nothing. Not one single thing. Either the whole firm has been told to clam up or I'm losing my touch.'

'So what did I tell you? Sinister happenings!' Tamara declared. 'Now do you believe me?'

'I think probably I do,' Roger mused. 'I have the urge to write an article. Let's flush them out, shall we?' He grinned at Tamara and she almost rubbed her hands in glee. It was exactly what she wanted and she had not even had to ask. The paper came out on Friday and then the balloon would go up.

Later in the day she had the chance for more action. She began to spread the word very carefully and she could not have done better than start with her first customer after lunch—Mrs Prost.

'How you're putting up with this noise and dust I can't think, Tamara,' Mrs Prost commiserated. 'My heart goes out to you.'

As it didn't go out to many, Tamara felt duly honoured, but she took the opportunity at once.

'Well, it's not going to concern us for much longer,' she confided. 'At the end of March we're all moving out. I just don't know how any of us are going to cope with the after-fashion-show rush.'

'Moving out? What do you mean?' Duly startled, Mrs Prost fixed Tamara with a disapproving eye. She above all felt attached to this place. Not many people could afford the clothes. There were no parking difficulties and it gave one a feeling of being very select to walk calmly across the park and browse through London-bought clothes.

'Why, didn't you know?' Tamara asked with a startled look of her own. 'The leases expire at the end of the month and Tysak Holdings have bought the whole mews. Of course, we won't be homeless,' she added with a wry grimace. 'We're being offered temporary accommodation. Those new shops in Charles Street.'

'Charles Street! My dear, it's so down-market there. One hesitates to shop at all in that end of town. How long do you expect to be there?'

'Ah!' Tamara said with a knowing look at her. 'We're *supposed* to be coming back here after a while, but then again, as you know quite well, Tysak Holdings develop property. I would imagine that such firms are always land-hungry.'

'But this is Edwardian property. Surely the council...'

'Only the façade has an order on it,' Tamara informed her with studied gloom. 'Who knows about the back?'

Mrs Prost was too stunned to reply. She picked up her carefully tied box and simply walked out, shattered by the blow, and Tamara knew she would not have to

do any more spreading of the word. Mrs Prost was a
gossip *par excellence*. Things were moving. Tamara
hummed a little ditty and made herself a good cup of
coffee. She felt like a trouble-maker but it did nothing
to alarm her conscience. Jason Tysak deserved all that
was coming to him and she felt it was plenty. She knew
this town, he did not. There was a great element of
snobbery in some quarters. Powerful tongues would wag.

Next day the shop never seemed to be empty and,
although they all bought something, Tamara had not
one doubt about this sudden rush of trade. The wives
of the local businessmen seemed to be thronging in. That
peculiar phenomenon 'word of mouth' was in action.

She kept her remarks very discreet. She wasn't going
to give Tysak a chance to take any action against her,
but he would not be able to sue her for a wistfully
shrugged shoulder, a wry smile, a drooping mouth. By
the end of the day she had a small army of wealthy supporters, every one of them incensed on her own behalf,
and she knew that the timing was perfect. In two days
it would be Friday and the paper would be out. It would
stir things up very nicely.

It did. Tamara read Roger's article eagerly. She could
not have wished for better even if she had put words
into his mouth. The heading was eye-catching—'Mystery
of the Mews'. One or two hard questions were asked.

What is the future of our beautiful Edwardian end of
town? This paper understands that the refined and
lovely Lancrest Mews has been bought up by Tysak
Holdings. The council are very coy about the whole
matter, and it does spring to mind that the Old Manor
Hotel, another Tysak property, stands at the end of
the mews. A coincidence? Perhaps it is time that Tysak

Holdings set a few minds at rest and stated their aims.

It went on in like vein, and Tamara read every word earnestly. There was a lovely photograph of the mews as it had been in Edwardian times, another at present day, with the park and the tall trees included. The third picture slot was empty except for a huge black question mark. Without any further words it asked what Tysak Holdings were up to, and Tamara could not have been better pleased. It would inspire her small army of supporters, infuriate Jason Tysak if he was still here and maybe, just maybe, he would back off and leave things alone.

All day it rained miserably. The park was almost invisible beneath the lash of rain. Water ran down the windows, and long before closing time it was quite, quite dark. Tamara let Janet go early because the rain was keeping custom to the minimum and, in any case, Janet had a bus to catch.

The park was soggy with water, very depressing, and if this continued there would be floods in many places. Apparently the river in the next town was ten feet above normal, the rain adding to the volume of water already brought by the melting snow on high ground. The local news had given out flood alerts for several places, but at least this town was safe, well into the hills.

Tamara started cashing up and doing the stock list. Things were going so well with her campaign that a little rain was not about to dismay her, or even a lot of rain, but she hadn't got very far when the sound of the bell had her going back into the shop. Whoever was out on an evening like this must be really desperate.

She had to admit that her heart did a very wild swing as she saw Jason Tysak standing in the doorway. He

looked even taller. He had a white belted raincoat on
with the collar turned up, his shoulders were wet and his
dark hair gleamed with water. Everything about him
showed that he had walked across the park to get here
and it had not pleased him at all.

He was furious, and Tamara had not one doubt as to
why even if he had not had a copy of the local paper,
wet and folded, in his hand. He slammed the door and
advanced menacingly, co-ordinated, graceful, powerful
movement that scared her. There was something about
him tonight that said 'aggressive male sex' and she was
hard pressed not to race into the back room and lock
the door.

'Is this your doing?' he grated, none of the amused
appraisal in his eyes that had annoyed her at their first
meeting. He was not trying for sexual superiority other
than giving the impression he would like to beat her
soundly.

'I'm not a journalist,' Tamara assured him haughtily.
She fully intended to stand her ground and not let the
trembling in her legs show at all. It evidently was not
what he wanted to hear because the dark eyes narrowed
ominously and he came even closer.

'No,' he rasped, 'you're a trouble-maker, a professional nuisance and a very ill-informed one! My phone
has been ringing all day about this article. I don't know
how you wheedled them into doing it, but I haven't forgotten your threats, Miss Rawson.'

Tamara had to admit it was a relief to realise he did
not yet know of her campaign of gloomy speculation.
As far as she could tell, most of the wives of the
'important' men in town had been in Impressions and
shown real annoyance towards Tysak Holdings; some

had almost shown spite. She really shuddered to think how he would look if he knew about that.

'People have a right to know what's going on in their own town, under their very noses!'

'*Nothing* is going on! Let me remind you that I got you the temporary accommodation. It was not necessary at all but then, of course, I didn't realise I was dealing with an immature and imaginative pest. I have no obligation to rehouse any of you. What then, Miss Rawson? Where do you go from here?'

'Straight to the paper,' Tamara assured him tartly, her head held at a defiant angle. 'Threats! That sounds like good copy to me.'

'Keep out from under my feet!' he warned angrily, his eyes flashing over her face as if the sight of it annoyed him considerably. 'So far it's just a minor irritation. Keep this up and you have a battle on your hands. I'll make you damned uncomfortable!'

'Menacing remarks merely anger me,' Tamara stated, although her legs felt more than a bit shaky by now. It was daunting to say the least to face his anger at close quarters. 'I can make this town too hot to hold you.'

'Can you?' There was a sudden sinister softening to his tone and his eyes bored into hers until she had to fight not to look away. 'If you can get the better of me, Miss Rawson, you surely would deserve a big reward. I'll have to see what I can come up with.'

'People,' Tamara said breathlessly, 'are behind me.'

'And that's just where they'll be when you're in the firing line—*right* behind you!'

She didn't get the chance to take him up on the subject of loyalties because he glared balefully at her and stalked out like a cougar, leaving an atmosphere behind him that was electric. Tamara felt as if she had had a brush with

a war party. For a second she couldn't move at all, and
her breathing was just returning to normal when the door
opened and he was there again.

'Why don't you lock the damned door?' he snapped.
'It's black and raining outside and every other shop in
the mews is closed. Some adversary you're going to make
when you haven't the sense to protect yourself.'

'Are you thinking of robbing me?' Tamara asked with
trembling bravado.

'Have you anything worth taking?' His dark eyes slid
over her, suggestively derisive, and this time as he
slammed the door she rushed across and locked it, her
cheeks flaming. Chauvinistic humour of a sexually op-
pressive variety! It would all be noted against him when
she won.

The next act in the drama really startled Tamara and
left her wondering just what she had started. The local
paper did a lot of printing, and Roger rang to ask if she
had seen the leaflets.

'What leaflets?' Instantly she was wary, her heart
giving a little lurch that was becoming quite a familiar
feeling since she had met Jason Tysak.

'About the mews.' Roger gave that sarcastic little laugh
he used when he knew somebody was hedging. 'I know
you got someone to order them. No need to be coy with
me, though, sweetie.'

'I'm not being coy!' Tamara stated emphatically. 'I
don't think I'd know how anyway. As to leaflets, as I
don't know, you'd better tell me.'

'I'll read one out. Heading: "Our Edwardian
Heritage". Substance:

　　Do we intend to ignore the fact that once again de-
velopers are changing the face of our town? In the

past the residents of this town have said nothing as
acres of land have been taken for buildings, many of
which have merely added to the traffic problems,
seriously inconveniencing the people who live here.
Several buildings have been erected that do not in any
way blend into the old and mellow grace of this town.
It is too late now but not too late to stop another piece
of our history being ruined. Lancrest Mews is at risk
at this moment, and where will this sort of thing stop?
Write to your council and demand explanations.

Et cetera, et cetera.'

Roger deliberately let the silence hang, and, the longer
it went on, the more glowing became Tamara's cheeks.

'I know your name isn't on the order form,' he murmured in amusement, 'but it's just your fighting style.
Want to tell me about it?'

'I honestly don't know a thing about it,' Tamara got
out in a rush of embarrassment. It was just such an action
she had wanted, but, after facing Jason Tysak the week
before, she was not now so very sure of her ground. He
would put it down to her too, and she wasn't altogether
certain about what he would do. For a start, there was
the matter of temporary accommodation. 'Who ordered
the leaflets?'

'Mrs Prost, on behalf of her committee.'

'*What* committee?' There was the decided feeling of
things getting out of hand, and Tamara knew right then
that the whole thing was about to run away with her,
dragging her along behind.

'The committee to save the mews,' Roger informed
her with utmost authority. 'There's a whole bevy of ladies
with their names printed clearly in ink, and you're an
honorary member, in brackets.'

'I don't know anything about it!' Tamara protested, feeling incredibly guilty because, after all, she had started this with her campaign of whispered gloom and it was clear that Roger didn't believe a word of it. Neither would Jason Tysak.

'Be that as it may, sweetie,' Roger murmured, 'we printed two thousand copies and they've been collected. It was a rush job.'

'Two thousand! Look, you had no right to let my name be on anything I didn't know about!'

'Stop pulling my leg, Tamara,' he laughed. 'You were the one who launched this whole campaign against Tysak Holdings. Anyway, business is business. Let me know when you want any further action.'

Tamara stared out at the dismal scene from the back of the shop as Roger rang off. It was still pouring with rain. It had rained all weekend, and today there had been no architect around, no surveyor. She dreaded the thought of Jason Tysak's coming round. Taking on Tysak Holdings had seemed a battle with a faceless enemy, little people against a money-machine. Jason Tysak did have a face, though, and he would be showing it angrily when he heard about the leaflets.

She wasn't too sure what he would do. He worried her with his dark eyes and his air of well-contained savagery. And then again there were the others. Would he take it out on the other leaseholders? She had never consulted them about her campaign.

She walked into the shop with a forced smile and faced the two remaining customers, both of whom were just going into the changing-rooms.

'It's a terrible night,' one of them pointed out. 'The river's up again.'

'Well, we're safe here,' Tamara consoled soothingly. She didn't feel any too safe. Tonight she would leave when Janet left. She wasn't about to let herself be trapped here with Jason Tysak. She might not escape from round two unscathed.

He out-thought her and outmanoeuvred her with ease. He walked in two seconds later, and she didn't have to be told that he had seen a leaflet; he just slammed one down on the glass-topped counter and glared at her.

'This, I take it, is your declaration of war!' he rasped.

She could hardly show surprise at the sight of the leaflet. Roger had not long ago finished enlightening her, and her guilty looks said all he wanted to know.

'Nothing to say for yourself, Miss Rawson?' he enquired caustically. 'Do you realise how much like a guilty child you look? Clearly you never grew up and didn't know when to stop having tantrums. Right now a copy of this leaflet is with my solicitor. If I can find one single thing to get you on I'll make you sorry you ever even saw Lancrest Mews. And you can all forget the temporary accommodation!'

Until that moment Tamara was so filled with guilt and confusion that her ready tongue had deserted her. The others were about to be blamed for her actions, though, and that came under the heading of unfair. She came to furious life.

'In the first place, I had nothing to do with those leaflets,' she stormed. 'I only just found out about them myself. In the second place, even if I had asked for them to be printed and distributed, it's got nothing at all to do with the others in the mews. You can't punish them because of me!'

'You'll find I can do exactly as I like, Miss Rawson!' he gritted, his eyes flashing furious sparks. 'In future, life is going to be very uncomfortable for all of you. And if they want to place blame, tell them to take a good long look at you!'

'It's not fair!' She glared up into his furious face, so much smaller than him in spite of her model's height.

'*Fair*! What do you know about being fair?' He raised his voice to an actual roar, and Tamara suddenly became aware that there were two customers in the changing cubicles and that Janet was standing all wide-eyed and astounded at the side of the room. She came round the counter speedily and grabbed his arm, quaking at the feel of taut, angry muscles.

'You can't make a scene here, Mr Tysak! This is my establishment and I must ask you to leave.'

She was so anxious to get him out of the shop and out of the hearing of the customers, both of whom had reappeared in double-quick time, anxious not to miss this spectacle, that she kept on going towards the door, her impetus moving them both forward. It was only as she had the door open to the pouring rain that she realised he had allowed her to hustle him so far. His expression of astonished ferocity made her pause for a moment, and in that slight pause he took control of proceedings, stepping out into the rain, taking her with him and closing the door, everything about him assuring her of immediate violence.

'I would very much like to wring your beautiful neck!' he informed her vehemently. 'On the other hand, I'm not at all sure that you're quite in possession of your faculties. There's a good chance that your brain is only loosely attached to your body. In place of brutality, therefore, we'll try another lesson.'

So far the small curved, hard awning over the door had been sheltering them, and as he moved with deliberate menace it still continued to shelter him. Tamara, however, he thrust out into the rain, his arm lashing round her waist, his other hand tilting her head until the full force of the cold rain poured into her upturned face.

She had to close her eyes as the rain lashed at her like small cold pebbles, making her gasp for breath as if she were drowning, and then the rain was cut off as his dark head bent over hers, and her gasp turned to one of violent shock as his hard lips closed over hers in a furious and devastating kiss that momentarily made her feel faint.

It only lasted for a second but it seemed that she was drowning all over again, this time in the taste of a furious and powerful male animal. There was the unexpected tang of his skin, the tightening of his arms, the angry crushing of his lips against hers, and then he let her go, holding her for another second in the rain before pulling her back under cover.

Tamara stared at him blindly. Never in her whole life had anyone treated her like this. She felt humiliated and shocked, every single part of her was trembling and she could make no move to escape. Water was running down her neck from her hair, and he stood there, watching her coldly.

'Now you know not to play outside your league,' he grated, his dark eyes burning into her. 'Tomorrow you'll be hearing more from me.'

'I think you'll be hearing from me, or, rather, from my solicitor,' she managed shakily. 'I've just been physically assaulted right in front of my own premises with at least one witness.'

'Three witnesses actually,' he growled, slanting a look at the lighted interior of Impressions. 'What they saw was an admirer kissing you, Miss Rawson.'

'How dare you? They know what they saw, and when I get back in they'll be in no doubt.'

'Well, then, we'll have to make them have doubts, won't we?' he said with silky menace.

Before she could move Tamara found herself back in those strong, hateful arms and this time he turned her towards the light as his mouth came down on hers relentlessly. She tried to struggle but he had never doubted that she would and he held her implacably, his hand cupping her head beneath the red-gold hair now darkened by the rain. This time too he kissed her slowly and sensuously until her struggles faded and she murmured anxiously against his lips.

A quite terrifying burst of feeling hit her deep inside, somewhere between her stomach and her legs. It was a feeling she had never had before and it overwhelmed her. Somehow he knew and he drew her closer, settling her against him with an unexpected grunt of satisfaction, his strong body against the shuddering warmth of hers. All the fight had gone out of her and it was an almost brutal shock when he lifted his head and moved sightly away.

'Now tell them,' he advised sardonically as he released her slowly. 'One attack, perhaps. Two attacks— quite unlikely, especially as the victim was quite obviously willing.'

'Nobody will believe it,' Tamara gasped, shaking more than ever, her mouth still burning. She seemed to be pulsing with feeling, her breasts tight and swollen, pushed against the wet material of her dress almost painfully. 'They know me.'

'They'll know you even more tomorrow,' he promised softly. 'You're the girl who got everyone else tossed out into the cold wide world with no temporary accommodation. Notorious is the word that will fit you. Go inside, my dear Miss Rawson. You're quite wet.'

His eyes narrowed over her, taking in her bruised-looking lips and the way she held her body defensively, trying to hide the embarrassing evidence of her reaction to him. He stared into her eyes for a moment, his mind probing hers, and then he turned and walked off towards the hotel, walking as if he owned the mews—but then, he did.

Tamara gathered whatever courage and dignity she could muster and went back inside, not altogether surprised when the two customers looked carefully at anything but her. Thank goodness they were strangers, not Mrs Prost or any of her friends. In fact, Tamara had never seen either of them before and after this she doubted if she would see them ever again.

Janet's mouth was hanging open in comical surprise, but it was not at all amusing to Tamara and she went through to the back and tried to get dry. Her dress was ruined, wet through, and her hair was a mass of wild wet curls. Her heart was pounding with excitement, that terrible; unexpected feeling still deep inside her. She glared at herself in the mirror but looked speedily away when she saw the high spots of colour on her cheeks and the blazing amber light in her eyes.

She had been thoroughly and furiously kissed and she looked like that. She told herself it was assault, but her mind refused to agree with her at all. Jason Tysak had kissed her like an expert—gold-medal class—and she was still trembling with the power of it. She could still taste him on her lips and it didn't disgust her at all. For a second she had felt wanton, vividly alive. She was at a serious disadvantage in any war with him.

When she got home, Roger rang.

'Come out for a meal and talk tactics,' he wheedled, but she was not falling for that. Matters were out of her hands. She had done her worst and it was all going wrong. The whip hand was firmly with the opposition. If he saw her out with Roger he would come to his own conclusions—and he would probably see her. He might even be lurking about, waiting to inflict further punishment.

Her cheeks flooded with colour when she admitted reluctantly that it had not exactly been punishment. For a few seconds she had liked it just a little too much, and she had the distinct impression that he had ended up feeling even more annoyed than when he had started. She had not forgotten the way his eyes had flashed over her and then probed her mind before he had walked off. Why it should have annoyed him, she didn't know. He appeared to have all the advantages at the moment.

'Tamara? Try to answer before I go mad,' Roger ordered in an intrigued voice. 'Why the unearthly silence? Come out for a meal.'

'I'm indisposed,' she muttered dully.

'You mean, you're hiding?' Roger enquired mockingly. 'Where's that redheaded courage?'

'I'm not a redhead,' Tamara pointed out furiously, 'and you just don't know what trouble I'm in with this leaflet business.'

'Whatever it is, the editor will back you,' he said soothingly, but Tamara was in no mood to be soothed. She rang her mother as soon as she could get rid of Roger, and told her the whole story.

'You just might have to apologise, darling,' Susan Rawson pointed out quietly. 'It might be the only way to save your accommodation.'

'I will not apologise to that—that heathen! In any case,' she added more quietly, 'he wouldn't listen.'

'How do you know?'

'Because he's a savage with pots of money,' Tamara said lamely. She had not enlightened her mother about this evening's final happenings. It was something she could well do with forgetting. She wasn't too sure if Janet had believed her furious explanation. Janet had seen episode two.

It was difficult to sleep because she kept on reliving the latter half of the event, and, the more she pondered it, the more she was filled with shame at her final submission. She had simply given in! Never in her life had she been kissed in that hateful, devouring, sensuous way. It was degrading, and somehow he would pay for it. She fell asleep in the middle of new plans.

Next day found Tamara beset on two fronts. She had a call to make before she went to work and Janet was to open up. By the time Tamara arrived trouble was well under way. There were closed signs on the four shops and she walked into a heated discussion between friends.

'Why are we all closed?'

Inside Impressions her elegant gilt-edged chairs were occupied by her neighbours, and Janet stood anxiously watching.

'We all had telephone calls this morning, Tamara,' Edwina Brown said severely. 'Tysak Holdings are threatening to refuse temporary accommodation unless we can control you.'

'What?' Tamara stared at them, outraged. 'Control me? Did Jason Tysak...?'

'His solicitor,' Kenneth Dennison informed her with an equally severe look. 'And it was useless to point out that we knew nothing about your battle with Tysak. Apparently we sink or swim together.'

'It was very naughty of you, Tamara, to act in this unilateral manner,' Eric Simpson murmured quietly. 'You may be able to stuff your clothes into a warehouse and wait this out, but a hairdressing salon must keep on going. This very morning I've had to cancel my first two appointments to deal with this.'

'We all need to keep on going,' Edwina snapped with a disgruntled look at Eric for his gentle remonstration. 'The fact is, Tamara, that you've landed us all in this and it's up to you to get us out of it.'

'You'll have to apologise,' Kenneth Dennison stated emphatically. 'You may very well be able to afford to wait this out, but I can't afford any such thing.'

'Neither can I,' Tamara seethed. 'What makes you think we'll be back here finally, in any case?'

'Tysack Holdings assured us that——'

'Tysak Holdings is Jason Tysak!' Tamara fumed. 'It's not some big, benevolent being in the sky. It's a man, a very unpleasant man.'

'I'm beginning to think there's something between you and Tysak,' Edwina mused with a glance at Janet, who went quite red-faced.

'There is,' Tamara snapped. 'It's called bitter enmity.' She glared at Janet but decided to let this little bit of passed-on gossip go by at the moment. 'Look,' she said flatly, 'I did not order those leaflets and that's what has infuriated him. I knew nothing about them. I can't get them back—they're already delivered. Nothing is going to calm him down.'

'Well, you've got to try,' Kenneth Dennison said firmly. 'You started this, Tamara. I for one will leave it to your conscience.'

They walked out together, although Eric did stop to pat Tamara's arm in a placatory manner. The other two, though, waited pointedly at the door and he didn't have the nerve to stand up to them. Tamara had the decided feeling that she had been sent to Coventry by a vote of two out of three.

'Open up for business, Janet,' she ordered bleakly and got straight on the phone. Her mother was right. She would have to apologise, and if she didn't do it now it would choke her.

When she finally got through to Jason Tysak she was enraged at his attitude, which was one of ironic amusement.

'You really want to speak to me, Miss Rawson?'

'Surely you expected it? Your solicitor has been on the phone bright and early to my neighbours. He threatened, of course, but then, you already know all this, Mr Tysak.'

'And you're ringing to complain.'

'I'm ringing to apologise,' Tamara said tightly. There was just the edge of threat in that deep, dark voice and she wasn't going to get anywhere if she kept this tone up. Besides, the sound of it made her tremble a bit, and it was a new and unwelcome experience.

'You sound most unapologetic. Reprimanding would perhaps describe your manner best.'

'I'm apologising. I'm sorry, I——'

'You're not at all sorry, Miss Rawson,' he interrupted silkily. 'You're furiously annoyed that you've lost the battle.'

'I am sorry that I——' Tamara began again, clenching her fist with inner rage, but this time he interrupted with steel in his voice.

'You may apologise to my face, Miss Rawson,' he stated coldly. 'I expect to see you in my office in fifteen minutes.' He just put the phone down, and Tamara stared at it grimly, her golden eyes narrowed. He was rubbing it in with a vengeance. He intended to see her squirm. Well, she wouldn't!

CHAPTER THREE

THE atmosphere was subtly different when Tamara arrived at the house on Victoria Crescent. There was a tight air about the girl downstairs that told Tamara she was the cause of much trouble, and although she was sent immediately upstairs the girl avoided her eyes and looked very much as if she was hiding. It all proved how bad a boss Jason Tysak was, as far as Tamara was concerned. Obviously he had taken it out on everyone here.

Miss Phillips looked at her reprovingly and then spoke into the machine on her desk.

'Miss Rawson is here, Mr Tysak.'

There was a sort of angry grunt from next door, and Miss Phillips nodded at Tamara.

'You're to go straight in.' Evidently she was skilled at deciphering disgruntled signals, and she sat down at her own desk speedily with no intention of showing Tamara into the inner sanctum.

He was contemplating the crescent again but this time he was standing, hands in his pockets, his jacket slung over the back of his chair, and he turned slowly as she came into the room, closing the door behind her. She was not about to allow Miss Phillips to hear any apologies.

He stood and looked at her steadily, a frown on his dark face as he noticed the wings of defiant colour across her cheeks. He didn't need to be told how she felt—it was all there in her tawny eyes. She was more angry than usual, in fact, and some of the anger was directed at herself. At the sight of him she had gone weak at the knees. It was a feeling she would fight with every bit of nerve she could summon up.

'There's nothing subdued about you, is there, Miss Rawson? I imagined you were here to apologise, but as far as I can see you're even more angry than you were the last time you came to this office.'

'Did you expect me to be pleased?' Tamara asked in a choked voice. 'You know perfectly well that I'm here under duress. Obviously you're not used to people who fight back.'

'There was never anything to fight about, Miss Rawson,' he pointed out grimly. 'You have brought this whole thing down to an undignified skirmish in public. You have also reduced me to acting the part of a chauvinistic male.'

It was obvious what he was talking about and Tamara's face flushed more wildly. Memory was a terrible thing and she had plenty of it right now.

'You did all that by yourself. And don't say I drove you to it either. Nobody has ever treated me like that in my life before!'

'Perhaps that's what's wrong,' he muttered, his eyes roaming over her moodily. 'You've obviously been spoiled. Being beautiful is not a passport to behaving exactly as you like. Perhaps this little episode will help to straighten you out.'

'I can do without the moral lecture, thank you. I came to apologise—as ordered.'

'Then begin, Miss Rawson,' he invited sternly. 'Please sit down.'

'I prefer to stand.' Tamara stared at him with great dislike, although it was difficult to juggle her feelings. If anyone deserved her complete annoyance it was him.

He had caused her a great deal of trouble, and moreover
he had humiliated her. Even so, her heart was hammering alarmingly each time those dark eyes swept over
her in that intent, brooding manner. His size and his
looks, his very masculine presence gave him an enormous
advantage that she had not counted on when she had
started this battle.

The men she had met before with looks anything approaching his had had an air about them of smug satisfaction, certain knowledge of their male beauty that
had quite nauseated her. Jason Tysak seemed completely unaware of his good looks. He was totally at ease
with his lithe body, his daunting power, and clearly never
thought of it at all. He stood scowling at her as if he
could not make up his mind what to do with her, and
she knew perfectly well that he was actually quite above
this sort of battle. He found it distasteful and she was
pretty sure he was ashamed of his furious action the last
time they had met.

'I—I'm sorry that I infuriated you,' she said rapidly,
her carefully rehearsed little speech having fled from her
mind now that she was actually facing him. His dark
brows rose ironically.

'My fury is a little aside we can forget about,' he assured her. 'It is the actual hard damage you're here to
atone for, Miss Rawson. You set out to blacken my name
and you've made a damned good job of it so far. Let
me point out to you that a business like mine requires
a great deal of good will. When I buy land and put in
plans a certain standard is expected. If word of this
sordid little battle spreads beyond this small patch then
questions will be raised whenever I appear on the scene.
Tysak Holdings will be looked at with a very suspicious

eye by all planners. It is not merely your irritating presence that annoys. I have to think of my firm.'

Tamara sat abruptly and faced him as he leaned back in his chair and eyed her sternly.

'I—I never thought... This was not meant to be anything but a personal...'

'Attack? Surely it is a personal attack? You succeeded very well and very swiftly. I imagine that having the local editor as a boyfriend helps enormously, but somebody has organised the wealthy ladies and I'm quite sure it was you. A small, meek and quite unwilling apology will not do. I want something of more substance.'

'What do you mean?' Tamara's colour came and went. It was rather alarming too that he now knew her relationship to Roger, even if he had got it partly wrong. He had checked up on her. It made her feel very vulnerable, almost ready to run for cover.

'Your honour is quite secure, Miss Rawson,' he informed her pithily, his eyes on her flustered face. 'I require an assurance that you will stop this battle at once. I also require a written apology.'

'I—I'll send you a letter,' Tamara said, her tawny eyes beginning to look annoyed again at his tone. She had known he meant to rub it in and this was it. Still, she had to do it, otherwise they would all lose their accommodation.

'You will send a letter of apology to the paper,' he insisted grimly. 'You made this a public battle. You will apologise in public. I want to see your apology printed clearly in this week's edition—arrange it with your boyfriend.'

'What?' Tamara jumped up and stared at him wildly. 'I can't do that! Roger... the editor will be furious. He's written about this too. Why aren't you going after him?'

'I rely on you to take the wind out of his sails, Miss Rawson. You started this. You will finish it.'

'And what about my customers? They're right behind me in this. They—they even started a committee.'

'I'm well aware of that,' he pointed out irritatedly. 'They can disband it.'

'I'll lose their custom. I rely on them.'

'You have an exclusive establishment, as I understand it. If they want the clothes they'll come back. When you're a little older and a little wiser you'll learn to think before you act.'

'Did you think before you acted the other night?' Tamara enquired furiously. 'Did you consider the odds before you pushed me out into the rain and—and...?'

'Kissed you?' He looked up at her quizzically. 'No. I acted on impulse. Most unusual for me. You infuriated me. You've probably been kissed by some frustrated male before, however, or don't you leave them frustrated?'

'I did not come here to be insulted!' Tamara snapped, blushing like a rose.

'No. You came here to be told what to do. I've told you: I want a written apology in this week's paper. Otherwise you all lose your temporary accommodation.'

'It was never going to be temporary,' Tamara said bleakly, not seeing any way out of this humiliation. 'I know you intend to build on to the mews.'

'I do,' he said softly. 'I intend to amalgamate everything into one very attractive unit dominated by the hotel.'

'You're a snake in the grass!' Tamara glared at him, not one bit pleased that all her forebodings had come to pass. She was blocked at every turn and there was no chance that he would play fair.

'And what are you? A bird in the hand?' He pressed the buzzer on his desk. 'The letter, Miss Rawson. I look forward to reading it. Show Miss Rawson out,' he added with a smile at Miss Phillips, who now stood waiting. 'And see that she gets in to see me any time she needs to, while I'm here.'

Tamara never wanted to see him again. She had been soundly beaten, roundly chastised for the first time in her life, and she walked out without looking at him, very well aware that those dark eyes followed her progress with satisfaction. *That's* how you got to be a millionaire. You had to have no scruples. You could lie with no regrets and you beat people to their knees without a qualm. You kissed the enemy even—if the situation required it.

She was barely inside the shop when Edwina came rushing round.

'Who's minding your store?' Tamara asked sourly, still smarting from the dressing down she had received from Jason. Edwina, though, was in a placatory mood.

'I know you didn't want to do this, Tamara,' she said coaxingly, 'but it's our livelihood. If you hadn't gone then we would all have lost and we're not so young as you. You *did* go, I assume?'

'I went,' Tamara said grimly, casting a frown at Janet, who had obviously been passing on information again. Janet was trying to signal her but she ignored it. She was more than a little miffed with Janet.

'So do we keep our temporary accommodation?' Edwina asked anxiously.

'When I've apologised.'

'But I thought that's where you'd been? Didn't you go to apologise to Tysak?'

'I went,' Tamara assured her fiercely. 'It won't do. He wants a written apology and he wants it in the next edition of the paper. Only a public apology will do. He intends to humiliate me.'

'Oh, Tamara! We never meant this to happen. I mean, fair's fair; what exactly have you done other than question his motives? You didn't put the notices around, after all.'

Janet was squirming, and it became obvious as to why when there was a flurry of silk and Mrs Prost stepped out of one of the changing-rooms, half in and half out of a sugar-pink evening gown.

'My dear, I couldn't help overhearing. This is disgraceful! You have friends in this town and we'll not allow you to be humiliated like this.'

Edwina looked stunned, and Janet pursed her lips in an 'I tried to warn you' attitude, but Tamara was quite past caring. She felt deeply depressed by all this. There was a feeling of her having been manoeuvred by more than one party. She was no longer sure who her friends were, or even if she had any at all.

'I apologise publicly or we all lose our temporary accommodation, Mrs Prost,' she explained wearily. 'In any case, I quite see his point. I could have really damaged his firm.'

Fairness made her admit it and they all looked at her as if she were in need of medical attention. Tamara Rawson did not capitulate so readily.

'He's browbeaten you!' Mrs Prost said furiously, studying Tamara's depressed expression. 'It can be done so easily to the young.' She stepped back into the changing-room, more on her mind now than the local ball, and in seconds the gown was handed out. 'Put this on my account, Janet,' she ordered, standing there in her slip, her tan from a recent trip to Bermuda gleaming expensively. 'I'll collect it later. I have things to do.'

None of them dared ask what things, but she told them anyway as she slid into her suit.

'Of course, you wouldn't know,' she assured them, 'but there's a public meeting tomorrow night at the Bounty Rooms. I did intend to make sure you were all there but now I can see it wouldn't be a good idea. Stay out of the limelight, Tamara, and leave everything to me.'

'Oh, I don't think... It wouldn't be wise...' Tamara began anxiously, but Mrs Prost was in full cry.

'This is town business,' she reminded them all firmly, 'a civic affair. Many important people are quite outraged. I'll keep you informed.' She picked up her coat and swept out, determination written across her face, and Tamara sank to one of her gilt-edged chairs.

'He'll think I did it,' she said worriedly. 'He'll think I came straight back and went to Mrs Prost and gang. You can't blame me for this, Edwina. You were right here and you saw how things escalated. A steamroller couldn't stop that woman.'

'I tried to warn you,' Janet began.

'Why didn't you tell us right out?' Edwina asked with annoyance, but then looked embarrassed. 'I'm sorry, Janet. It's wicked to take it out on you. I caused it, after all, darting in here and starting straight off. What to do now?'

'There's only one thing to do,' Tamara said reluctantly. 'I'll have to let him know. If we're to stand any chance at all I've got to warn him.' She grimaced uneasily. 'I can see myself getting deeper and deeper into this because if that woman finds out I've warned him she'll be on to me at once.'

'Well, it depends where your loyalties lie,' Edwina said uneasily.

'They certainly don't lie with Jason Tysak!' Tamara snapped, but inside she was not altogether sure. She seemed to have started a whirlwind of destruction and she had a nasty feeling that the strong and powerful would be the winners in spite of people power. That let her out completely. Jason Tysak and Mrs Prost's committee would be locked in deadly combat, and she would be crushed in the middle.

Edwina gave her an unexpected peck on the cheek.

'I'll let the others know,' she muttered, and darted out before Tamara could stop her. The fewer people who knew, the better. Janet looked utterly miserable and Tamara remembered her unswerving loyalty for the whole time she had been here.

'Go for your lunch, Janet,' she ordered with a wry smile. 'I'll do my grovelling in private.'

'I'm sorry, Tamara——' she began, but Tamara stopped her.

'I brought all this down on my own head.'

'You were only defending us,' Janet sniffed unhappily, collecting her coat.

True, Tamara thought bitterly as Janet left. She hadn't told them that he was going to take the whole mews; she just hadn't had the heart. They would be stuck in the new accommodation forever. It was a good job she had kept silent. Mrs Prost was riding high as it was. She picked up the phone with a great deal of reluctance.

'I sincerely hope you're not about to tell me you've changed your mind about that letter,' he said threateningly when she got through to him.

'No. I have news for you.' Tamara struggled to get her nerves under tight control. At the sound of his voice she had started to tremble, an altogether new experience, and she didn't quite know how to break the news to him anyway.

'Go on,' he invited darkly after an ominous pause.

'I—I just found out that there's a meeting tomorrow night at the Bounty Rooms,' she informed him anxiously. 'The—the committee have called it and it's a public meeting and—and it's about——'

'I haven't any doubts at all what it's about!' he assured her caustically. 'When did you arrange this, Miss Rawson?'

'I didn't!' Tamara protested. 'I already told you that the leaflets and the committee are nothing to do with me. There are some powerful people in this town and matters were taken right out of my hands. I never meant——'

'You never meant to be caught?' he enquired menacingly. 'You declared war on me at our first meeting. And why are you warning me of this?'

'I—I thought it only fair...'

'You mean, you've changed sides? Better think about that. I might lose this battle. Place your bets very carefully, Miss Rawson. Being disloyal is a tricky business and, in any case, you lose, whoever wins.'

'I'm not being disloyal!' Tamara protested, not at all sure whether she was or not. He didn't have to point out that she was in a no-win situation.

'Forget about that letter to the paper,' he said suddenly as if everything else had passed him by. She had a picture of some furious thinking going on and she had to admit it scared her a little. She was out of her league, as he had said, and she acknowledged it silently.

'Are you going to—to toss us all out?' she asked miserably.

'Wait and see,' he rasped. 'Let's hope the suspense doesn't kill you. I know perfectly well that you're an impatient and wilful female, quite used to having all your own way. One of these days somebody is going to give you a very much needed spanking.'

He put the phone down and Tamara looked at herself in the mirror, astonished at her shaken appearance. Power was, after all, a frightening thing, and she knew he had been swiftly and silently planning even as she had talked. She would hate to be the woman in his life, she thought with a wild rush of idiotic thought.

The idea made her blush, even though there was nobody to see, because she remembered that kiss. It seemed to be lingering in her mind, coming back when least expected. If she could have lived that time over again she would have sat tight and kept her head down, simply waited for the crunch because in spite of her efforts the crunch would come and it would be worse than ever now.

They all had letters the next day, delivered by hand from the Tysak solicitors, and the news prompted an instant meeting.

'Did you get one of these?' Edwina asked breathlessly, coming in with Kenneth Dennison, Eric hard on their heels.

'Just now,' Tamara muttered, still too stunned to have any real reaction. Her mind seemed to have closed down.

'We're to stay here; no need to move at all,' Eric stated, telling them quite unnecessarily the contents of their letters. 'Apologies for any anxiety caused.'

'What do you think?' Edwina asked after a look at Tamara's face. 'You know him.'

'I've decided not to think at all in future,' Tamara assured her. 'As to knowing him, I don't. He's the quick brown fox.' Inside she knew he was more the big bad wolf but there was no need to wipe the happy looks from their faces. They were to stay here. For how long? Would the leases be renewed? Nothing had been said about that and she knew what they did not. He was taking the whole mews.

'We'll have to play it by ear,' she suggested lamely. 'Let's forget it for now, shall we? There's the fashion show to organise, after all, apart from the usual business.'

'I hope he doesn't change his mind after tonight's meeting,' Edwina muttered worriedly as the others left. 'I wonder if he's going to put in an appearance there?'

'Most unlikely,' Tamara stated flatly. 'Quite beneath his dignity.'

'Yes,' Edwina mused. 'I hear from Janet that he's like a film star to look at.'

'He'd only get the villainous parts,' Tamara assured her drily, that face coming back into her mind. Geronimo wasn't too far out after all.

'Well, I'll keep my fingers crossed,' Edwina promised as she left, and Tamara smiled weakly. Magic, however potent, would not work against that man. He was, as he had said, an irresistible force. As to the immovable object, hadn't she been crushed like a worm?

It was difficult to sleep that night. She felt like a small boat tossing at the edge of a storm, and next day as the phone rang she actually jumped.

'Thought I would just set your mind at rest, dear,' Mrs Prost said comfortably. 'You're all to stay there. No need to move to that dreadful temporary place after all. I expect he'll let you know.'

'Did he go to the meeting?' Tamara asked quickly before anything else could be said. She didn't want to have to tell that woman that they had all received letters the day before or she would be doing some rapid calculations.

'His solicitor,' Mrs Prost said grimly. 'I did think he might have come along but it matters not at all. Stage one has been successful. You're all safe for now.'

'Er—stage one?' Tamara enquired worriedly.

'Well, of course, this is not the end of the matter,' Mrs Prost said firmly. 'We'll be keeping an eye on things. You did say that he was probably going to take the whole of Lancrest Mews. I haven't forgotten.'

Well, it didn't matter anyway, Tamara mused as she put the phone down. They were all hanging on a slender thread and she knew it would break. She felt a rather grim smile surface as she contemplated his next move. Even if they were all out of it, he would have trouble. Mrs Prost and friends would be watching like hawks, attending every meeting at the council chambers, scouring the paper for planning details.

Maybe she should get out and look for other premises herself? She couldn't actually do that without telling the others of their very uncertain future. She would wait a while and see what happened.

The phone rang again as she was going back into the shop, and that dark, threatening voice had the usual effect on her.

'There will be workmen round today,' Jason Tysak said. 'Please inform the others. I will also be there this afternoon with my architect.'

'Why?' Tamara snapped like a terrier, and he sounded very patient, as if she were a half-wit, only barely controllable.

'I need to see the upper storeys of the mews. I had intended to do that while you all stayed in your part-time accommodation but, as matters have rather forced my hand, I'll get it done now.'

'We've got leases for now!' Tamara reminded him sharply.

'I have ownership,' he countered. 'Behave yourself, Miss Rawson. I've almost forgiven you. Don't stir up any more wrath, I beg you.'

She slammed the phone down and rang her own solicitor and got exactly nowhere.

'He has rights as owner, Tamara. So long as he doesn't make life too harsh, he must be allowed access. Providing he doesn't interfere with your business.'

'Workmen are coming,' Tamara said grimly.

'It depends on what they do. Keep me informed.'

He was backing off. She just knew it. She let the others know and they were as nervous as kittens about meeting the great man. Edwina actually looked in the mirror right then as if the time were already upon her, and Tamara had to stifle her feeling of frustration. She only hoped that Mrs Prost's cronies kept away today. One source of ultimate power was all she could cope with at a time.

She had no idea he had arrived until she looked up later and found him outside, studying the window. It brought on a nervous attack that had her scurrying into the back of the shop. When she went back he was still there and his architect was with him, their conversation most earnest. What were they contemplating? Did he intend to ignore all orders and knock the fronts down?

When he came in she stared at him in a mesmerised way that brought a quirk to his lips and a dancing light to the dark eyes.

'My architect, Miss Rawson,' he murmured, indicating his companion, who, to her surprise, didn't look a bit browbeaten. 'Tamara Rawson,' he added. 'You'll be seeing a fair bit of each other, so you'd better get on good terms.'

She was still staring as her hand was shaken vigorously by a fair-haired young man with very studious-looking spectacles. It was a bit stunning to realise that Jason Tysak knew her first name. Maybe he was having her investigated? If you added it all up he knew quite a lot of things about her.

'Er—how do you do?' she muttered vaguely. 'Do you need any help?'

'Just show us how to get upstairs,' Jason said. 'We don't want to get in your way.'

Everything he said seemed to mean something else and Tamara was not pleased with herself. Thus far nobody had ever made her feel nervous, but she was nervous now and admitted it. She was much too aware of him and it boded no good at all.

'There's a door in the back,' she offered, leading the way.

'Do you store things up there?' he asked quietly, stalking along behind her and making her skin go hot.

'No. I've never even been up there.'

'Then you're not an inquisitive female?' he enquired sardonically. 'Afraid of meeting Edwardian ghosts?'

'I find the living more repulsive,' Tamara informed him crossly. He was taking an attitude with her, she noticed. As if she were a silly little girl, and the way he kept his voice down to exclude the other man was worrying.

Janet had retreated to the very front of the shop. Soon she would be hiding in the changing-rooms. It was all too ridiculous.

As soon as they had the door unlocked she went back into the shop, and Janet sprang into action.

'I'll sort out the cups,' she said breathlessly. 'We must offer them a coffee.'

'We must do no such thing!' Tamara snapped, looking at her as if she were out of her mind. 'We want them out of here fast.'

'Diplomacy!' Janet whispered. 'If we get friendly with him he'll have a soft spot for us when the time comes to sign the leases again.'

Tamara shook her head in despair. She knew perfectly well it wasn't that at all. Janet was all goggle-eyed. The deadly arrow had struck. This morning he was all dark-eyed charm and coaxing humour.

'He's false and dangerous. Beware,' she warned. Janet just shot her a wary look and disappeared into the back.

There was a good deal of banging from aloft and not one customer came in. Tamara nipped round to warn Edwina of approaching invasion and left her very shaken. It was getting to be like a farce, she decided as she slipped back into the shop in time to see the two men come downstairs and encounter Janet with cups at the ready.

'That's very kind of you.' He beamed at Janet's flushed face. 'Janet, isn't it?'

All she could do was nod vigorously, and Tamara didn't know whether to be sorry for her or annoyed that she was keeping them here. The architect stood chatting, sipping his coffee, and Tamara was reminded that Janet had met him before, when he had invaded the premises with the others during her absence. She moved away from them all.

Jason strolled over to stand by the window, tall and dark at her side, as Tamara looked steadfastly out towards the park, trying to ignore him.

'Stop sulking,' he murmured almost in her ear. 'You've not lost entirely. You might even approve of what I'm going to do.'

'You mean, the part where you refuse to renew the leases?' she muttered crossly.

'I think I'll let you all worry about that for a little while,' he said derisively. 'You deserve it. Are they all trembling too?'

'I haven't told them about your plans,' Tamara snapped quietly. 'They couldn't take the shock. And I'm not trembling!' she lied vigorously.

'Really?' He looked down at her hands and she put them hastily into the pockets of her silk skirt, feeling hot and cold all over when he gave a low, dark laugh. 'Maybe we'd better raise our voices,' he suggested softly. 'This intimate whispering will make them suspicious. We wouldn't want any further rumours flying around, would we?'

'Why were you staring at the windows?' Tamara asked, taking his point and speaking much too loudly.

'We'll have to make some alterations.' He was grinning to himself, she noted, and her heart sank one more notch. 'I've been considering your complaints. Dust and noise. You'll have workmen here this afternoon or tomorrow morning. We'll double-glaze for you and put some excluders on the doors.'

'It will mean emptying the windows!' Tamara gasped. 'It takes hours to do these windows.'

'You can't have it all ways,' he pointed out with a shrug. 'I had intended to do all this while you were in your other accommodaton but, as events have overtaken us, we'll have to try and co-operate.' He looked down at her steadily and she bit her lip in deep vexation. He

intended to make her as uncomfortable as possible and
there was nothing she could do about it.

He nodded to her pleasantly, smiled nicely at Janet
and handed her his cup, and then they both left. Janet
was all a-dither, but Tamara fumed silently. There wasn't
a thing she could do and he had been perfectly right,
she did tremble when he was near. It must be rage, because it couldn't be anything else.

CHAPTER FOUR

WITH the fashion show looming ever closer, Tamara settled down to a good deal of organising. The spring clothes were delivered, and that too brought extra work. Mulling it over, she decided that her campaign had not been a total failure as things had worked out; after all, they were still here and, with the limelight well and truly on him, it was difficult to believe that Jason would risk tossing them out when the end of the leases arrived.

The alterations had been a nuisance. With great fortitude she had kept her temper as the men had informed her that it would take a little longer than normal because of the long bow windows. They had also endured a considerable time of deep chill as the excluders were fitted to the doors, which naturally had to be left wide open during the operation. It was all over now, though. There was less noise and no dust at all.

The window had been dressed again and everything cleaned up. She had half expected a visit from Jason to view the work, an almost excited anxiety about her at the thought, but obviously he did not sink to inspecting minutiae, and so far nothing was happening in the upper storeys of Lancrest Mews. Peace of a sort reigned.

Tamara sighed and gave one last look at the clothes before putting out the light and locking up. Janet had gone two hours ago. It was almost seven and black as coal outside. The rain had stopped for now but there was a damp chill in the air, and she had to skirt the park carefully to avoid being deep in squelchy grass. She pulled

her coat closer and hurried to her car, suddenly re-
gretting staying so late.

This was a very quiet part of town with few houses
nowadays. After the mews there was a church with high
stone walls, and the bright lights at the far end of the
road seemed to be a long way off tonight. It was a great
relief to reach her car and she sank thankfully inside,
berating herself for unnecessary nerves.

All her nerves came flooding back when the car refused to start. After several attempts she had to give up,
and then a choice had to be made: face the wet and dark
trip back to the shop and her own telephone, or walk
briskly towards the brighter lights and find a taxi there.
The lights won because she was suddenly not at all keen
on going back into the dark shop. She even felt a little
scared about crossing the park.

She set off at once, this unexpected attack of un-
easiness making her walk fast. It was almost like a pre-
monition and she kept her eyes steadfastly on the lights
of the town. Normally she was too busy planning and
thinking to be uneasy, but tonight for some reason even
her own footsteps sounded dangerously loud.

Her surge of thankfulness when she saw people approaching by the church turned to greater unease when
she realised that they were in fact four men. Midway
between the lights and the shop, it was either race back
or face it out, and she decided to keep going. She was
irritated with herself in any case for being here at this
time on a dark night, and also for giving way to feminine
fears. They were probably workmen going home, just
as she was.

They were youths, somewhere between seventeen and
nineteen, and their excited talking suddenly stopped as
they noticed her. She expected catcalls, maybe even some

very unpleasant suggestions, but she was not prepared to see them suddenly move line abreast and take up the whole pavement and some of the road. She was really frightened then.

There was no way out, though. She had the nasty feeling that if she ran back they would run too. She marched up, cold-faced, determined to walk right through them if they didn't move, sternly telling herself that she was afraid of nobody at all.

'Excuse me!' She made to pass between two of them and the others closed round as if it had been a worked-out plan of action. The most frightening thing was that they never spoke. Uncouth remarks, jeering, evil suggestions she could have coped with, but this determined silence was terrifying and her own tongue seemed to be stuck to the roof of her mouth as she backed towards the church wall.

She had heard of this sort of thing happening to others but she had never expected to be in any situation where it could happen to her. Living in London, she had known not to take risks, but here it had never occurred to her to be as wary.

She tried to push out of the circle and run, but the tallest one grabbed her sleeve and slammed her back against the wall. Fear came then in a great black cloud as she realised they had never even looked at her handbag.

'Let me go!' She suddenly found her voice and glared at them angrily, but she could see it was the last thing she should have done. She was slammed back to the wall again, banging her head, and one of them started to tug at her hair as the others began to laugh. Tamara made a great dive forward but she was caught and swung round roughly, and panic took hold of her, making her fight furiously. Trying to avoid their grasping hands, she had slipped to the ground and she kicked out at them, more terrified than ever.

Suddenly there was a roar of sound and a sleek red Jaguar slid to a halt beside them, the driver's door flung open violently, and after one threatening look at the man who got out the youths took to their heels. It was hard to threaten somebody who looked like a raging avenger, dark and furious, his powerful body swinging round the car towards them. They didn't wait to argue. Within seconds they were at the other end of the street and lost in the shadows.

'Tamara!' Jason strode forward and lifted her up. 'What in God's name are you doing here alone?'

She was shaking too much to speak, her jacket and skirt wet and dirty, tears of fright standing in her eyes, making them look too bright.

'Can you walk?' He put his arm around her and helped her to his car, standing for one frustrated second contemplating the road. 'I'd never catch them,' he muttered furiously, getting in beside her and starting the engine. 'Let's get you into the light and look at the damage. What did they do to you?' he grated.

'N-nothing. I was struggling to get free. Thank y-you for——'

'What were you doing there, for heaven's sake? In the daytime it's the height of calm respectability; at night it's just dark and lonely—dangerous for a woman by herself.'

'My car wouldn't start. I stayed late to work and then it wouldn't——'

'Why didn't you go back to the shop and phone for a taxi?' he demanded harshly, and it just about finished her off.

'I was scared to cross the park again. It was dark!'
She gave a little sob and his hand left the wheel to squeeze
her arm in a gesture of comfort and frustration.

'All right. All right. Interrogation over. Let's get you
to a brandy, a hot drink and a few bright lights.'

'If you could drop me at home,' she managed tearfully. She was cold, very cold, and the warm car did
nothing to help. Sheer chance had saved her and she
knew that perfectly well. If he hadn't been passing . . .

'I'll do that,' he said grimly, increasing his speed, and
Tamara sank further into the seat, shudders running over
her skin.

'I'll take you to my place,' he muttered, glancing
worriedly at her.

'No. I feel dirty. I—I've got to change and shower.
It's not because . . . I'm not refusing to go with you because I . . . You can come in with me.'

'There's not much chance of keeping me out,' he assured her flatly. 'You may think me chauvinistic, but I
don't sink to leaving a woman frightened, shivering and
all alone.'

He sounded a bit cross and Tamara didn't want that
at all. Foolishly she wanted to cling to somebody and
have a good cry. Being weak and feminine was just a
little new. So far in life her temper had spared her such
things, but right now she would have gladly admitted to
being feminine before a vast crowd of sceptics.

'I don't think you've chauvinistic,' she said in a catchy
voice. 'It's just that I had to fight you, and I lose my
temper easily. Sometimes I say anything to get my own
way.'

'I assumed as much. You're an infuriating female, but
right now you need some sort of solace.'

He never asked where she lived. He seemed to know a great deal because he just arrived at her flat as if he had been going there for ages, and Tamara was glad. She didn't even feel up to giving directions, and when he asked for her key she just handed her whole bag over and let him root around for himself. It was all she could do to stand upright. She felt more shocked by the minute. Maybe that was how shock worked?

Inside, he put on the lights, drew the curtains and then turned to look at her closely. She had a pretty good idea as to how she looked, and his lips tightened angrily as he saw her muddy skirt, her torn tights and her tousled hair. One of them had torn her blouse and there was a red scratch mark on her shoulder, quite visible as she struggled out of her leather jacket.

She caught sight of herself in the mirror and burst into tears, shaking uncontrollably as she lived it all again and knew perfectly well what he had saved her from.

'Just look at me!' she sobbed, and hard arms gathered her close to a strong warm body, holding her tightly until the frantic burst of misery dulled to small choked sounds.

'I'll get you a drink,' he said quietly, putting her away from him with great care and making her feel thoroughly ashamed about clinging to him so hard. She didn't have the right to do things like that. He was almost a stranger and she had been nothing but a nuisance to him since they had met.

'No. I need a shower first. It's all right, thank you. You can leave me now. I'll be fine.'

She didn't wait to see what he would do. She just rushed out of the room and into her bedroom, trembling, embarrassed and still scared. All the clothes were ruined. Those that just needed cleaning would be a constant reminder of tonight and she didn't think she would be

wearing them again. Under the shower, she noticed that
there were a few bruises on her legs and it took ages
before she felt sufficiently clean and free of the hateful
attention.

She wasn't looking forward to facing an evening alone.
Right now she could do with the ministrations of her
mother and a few caustic comments from her father.
She wouldn't ring them, though. Being so far away, her
mother would be frantic and she would never believe
that things were now all right.

If *he* were staying she would feel safe, comforted. The
thought made her scared and she pushed it aside. Why
should she trust his smiling eyes? They hadn't been
smiling as he had come and despatched those youths.
He had looked murderous and her attackers had seen
it. He was altogether too powerful to be a comfort. He
would have to be on your side to be that and he was
only here now because he had seen it all happening. He
would never be on her side at all.

When she stepped back into the sitting-room Jason
was just coming in from the kitchen with a tray of tea.

'Timed to perfection,' he congratulated. 'I have here
a good, hot brew.'

'Oh!' Tamara stood anxiously watching him. 'I—I
thought you'd gone. I didn't bother to get dressed. I
mean . . .'

His eyes slid over her from her newly washed hair to
the long blue robe that covered her down to her toes.

'You're dressed,' he concluded. 'Don't let my presence
upset you. I decided to stay,' he added, slanting her a
dark glance. 'I want to be sure you're all right.'

'Just a bit shaky. I can manage now, thank you.'

'Does that mean I don't get to pour the tea?'

'I'm not throwing you out,' Tamara murmured, looking away. 'I just don't want to be a nuisance to you and—and please don't tease me. I don't feel up to it at the moment.'

He poured the tea and handed her a cup, and from somewhere he had got a brandy. She hadn't been sure that there was any left. Clearly he had searched about but it did nothing to annoy her. His presence *was* comforting, she realised with a little shock of surprise. It must be his size. She curled up on the settee and he sat opposite, watching her.

'You look as if you need a good night's sleep, or a long cuddle,' he said quietly after a minute of assessing her. 'Want me to ring for your boyfriend?'

'No. He's not that sort . . . He'll want to make an issue of it,' she corrected hastily. She had been about to say that Roger wasn't that sort of boyfriend, that he wasn't even her boyfriend at all, but caution came to her aid at the last minute. 'He does run a paper, after all,' she added quickly. 'I can do without a scathing editorial on the subject of youth.'

'I see.' He looked at her steadily. 'So we have another secret now?'

'It was never intended, Mr Tysak——' she began, but he interrupted with a wry look at her.

'For heaven's sake! How long are you going to keep this up? Can't you bring yourself to call me by my name?'

'I should call you—Jason?' she blinked up at him. 'You can't expect that! If nothing else, you're my landlord.'

His grin was wide and infectious and made her feel like a very prim lady.

'How old-fashioned. I almost approve. A very well brought-up young lady. My friends call me Jason—why not give it a try?' he added softly.

Tamara felt too confused to answer, and she was still suspicious of him, in any case. She had the feeling that this was a man who had never placed a foot wrong. He invariably made her feel vulnerable—or furious. It was good to have him here now, though. All her trembling had come back, and her mind began to wander over the events of the evening. Suppose those youths knew where she lived? Suppose they...? She pulled herself up sharply and walked over to pour herself more tea.

Nothing had happened, after all, nothing serious. She was shaking so much that she spilled her tea, and once again felt tears rushing forward. They streamed down her cheeks and she wiped at them frantically, making no effort to resist when he pulled her down beside him and put his arm round her.

'Take it easy,' he murmured when she began to apologise in embarrassment. 'You've had a nasty shock and the thought of it will keep coming back for a while. Are you quite sure you don't want me to ring Hart? You should have somebody with you, and he seems to be the logical choice.'

Tamara just shook her head, still trying to stifle tears and completely unaware that she was burying her head against his shoulder. Even when he began to stroke her hair she felt nothing but comfort, her mind not quite there, fear still too deeply lodged inside.

'What about ringing a girlfriend, then?' he asked quietly.

'I—I don't really have one here. Since I came I've been too busy working, building the business...'

'Why don't you go away for a few days? Surely Janet could manage?'

'It's the fashion show.' Tamara suddenly realised just where she was, and she looked up, quite startled with herself, bemused that she found this man so good to be with. Maybe it was because he had rescued her? Her eyes, wide and amber, fastened on his dark face, and he looked down at her in silence, his arm still around her.

It was the way he looked that embarrassed her even more. She couldn't say he looked paternal, but he was obviously totally indifferent to having her here, so close.

'I—I'm sorry,' she managed, trying to sit upright. 'I'm really being quite impossible.'

'No, you're not.' His arm stayed where it was, around her shoulders, and his free hand brushed back her hair from her suddenly hot face. 'I knew you needed a shoulder to cry on. As you refuse to have Roger Hart here, then it has to be me.' His thumb ran along her jaw and he watched its progress almost thoughtfully.

'You must be hungry,' Tamara blurted out anxiously, blushing even more when his lips suddenly quirked. 'I— I mean . . . it's dinnertime . . . almost.'

'I don't think you're in any fit state to be taken out to dinner,' he pointed out, and she struggled quickly, feeling all manner of a fool.

'I wasn't asking to be taken out. I was thinking that you must be wanting to get back to eat and——'

'Want a pizza?' He looked down at her startled face and filled her with even more confusion.

'A—a pizza?'

'You know, those things with cheese and——'

'I know what a pizza is!' Tamara said emphatically, realising that he was laughing at her.

'Then shall we have a pizza? Shall we eat it here? I know just the place to get one.'

He didn't look the sort of person who went and fetched a pizza in, and Tamara bit her lip and looked away.

'You don't have to do this. I'm quite all right. You don't owe me any responsibility and—and...'

He stood swiftly, putting her aside with firm hands.

'I would like a pizza. I would like to eat it here with you. I'm even prepared to fetch it. Now are you on or are you not?'

'I'm on.' Tamara was suddenly smiling at him, her nerves very much settled.

'Good. A decisive female. It makes a nice change. And don't bother to dress up either,' he added severely. 'We need a plate each and two wine glasses. I'll collect the wine on the way back.'

He walked out, closing the front door firmly, and Tamara sat for a minute, feeling more bemused than ever. The force was there, definitely irresistible, but he wasn't at all worrying somehow. In fact, she felt as if she had known him for years. She put two plates to warm and then made a quick phone call to her mother, carefully avoiding all the latest traumatic events.

'And how is that dreadful Tysak man behaving?' Susan Rawson asked.

'Oh—er—he's not too bad, after all,' Tamara said lamely. 'I—I might have misjudged him.'

She felt her face glowing when her mother started to laugh, and she said goodbye very hastily before she was asked to explain her change of heart.

The pizza was surprisingly good, especially washed down by the wine. It didn't at all feel like a scratch meal, as Tamara pointed out.

'I feel as if I'm out to dinner,' she said in a musing voice, sharing her odd thoughts. 'Except for the fact that I'm not dressed.'

'You're very well dressed,' Jason assured her, his dark eyes running over her as she sat opposite. By now her hair had dried to a honey-gold shine and, although she had a tendency to shiver occasionally, she felt fairly well back to normal. He went on looking at her for a long time until she had to look away. 'You're a very beautiful girl, Tamara,' he said quietly.

'Thank you.' Suddenly it was difficult to talk. Until now they had spoken together with very little unease, but the air was charged with feeling right out of the blue and Tamara knew it was all coming from her. She wasn't really used to being with a man like this, not alone.

In London she had been careful and mostly she had been incredibly busy. Contrary to popular belief, a model of her standing was well chaperoned by an excellent agent. Dinners had been mostly business dinners with clients, her agent very much present and most discouraging when any dates were hinted at.

Tamara too had held herself aloof, her quiet home background shielding her rather than the other way around. Now she was here, alone with a very potent male. She wasn't even dressed, and the look in his eyes reminded her. He could sometimes look at her as if he could see into her head. Sometimes he let his eyes linger on her in a brooding way that set her heart hammering.

'How old are you, Tamara?' he asked abruptly.

'Twenty-four.' She looked up at the unexpected question and caught his slight grimace.

'So very young?'

'I expect you think that's why I behave as I do?' she asked with a flare of annoyance.

'I imagine tempers are a genetic characteristic,' he smiled. 'As to this evening—well, perhaps you're too trusting, or maybe you feel a little apart from the nastier side of life. Tell me about your family.'

It put her at her ease. There was nothing she liked better than talking about her home, about her mother's weird quirks of humour, her father's practice and his sometimes peculiar patients. It was a warm, loving atmosphere and she missed them daily.

'And why did you leave this cosy nest?' he asked quietly when her voice trailed away.

'To see the world. To try my hand at something for myself.' She shrugged and laughed a little miserably. 'I could have stayed there and helped my father. I could have worked in the nearest town, but I wanted some excitement and I wanted to get out from under their feet.'

'A bid for freedom?'

'No. A desire to give them time to themselves,' she said simply. 'Besides,' she added with a smile, 'I have a whole fistful of cousins who descend on us frequently. A bit harassing when you're a country doctor with hardly a minute. I'm giving them a breathing-space.'

'And then what?'

'And then I'll probably be unable to fit back in, a total misfit in any place. Doesn't that sound pitiful?'

'It sounds remarkably sensible...'

'For a twenty-four-year-old idiot?' she enquired wryly.

'Something like that.'

There was an atmosphere again and Tamara felt the need to keep the conversation going. He knew a great deal about her now. Some of the things he had apparently found out for himself when she had attacked him, but now she had told him even more. She knew nothing about him, though.

'Do you have a family?'

'Yes.' He didn't seem to be keen to talk about them at all.

'Do they live in England?' she persisted.

'My mother lives in Italy. My father lives in America. They divorced when I was fifteen and apparently they have no regrets.' He looked at her mockingly. 'I have a sister too, also divorced. It runs in the family, like your temper.'

'I'm the only one in the family with a temper,' Tamara assured him. She wanted to ask if he had ever been married but suddenly he looked quite forbidding and she just didn't dare.

He stood and began to clear the plates, and Tamara quickly jumped up.

'I'll do that. I'll make some coffee.'

He looked at her for a minute and then shook his head.

'I'll have coffee back at my place. I really must go now.'

It was something of a blow, and once again she felt guilty, as if she had kept him here and was still trying to hang on to him.

'Are you in some hotel?' she asked a bit desperately, realising she was wanting to hang on to his presence for as long as possible.

'I bought a house. I like the town and I don't have a house in England. I thought it was a good idea to set down a few roots.'

'Oh.' It gave her a good deal of pleasure to hear that and she felt her face growing hot. 'Miss—Miss Phillips said you weren't here much. She—she said that she didn't often have the pleasure.'

He started to laugh, very dark male laughter that sent a wave of awareness over Tamara's skin. Her face flushed to a warm apricot when she realised just what she had implied.

'Believe me, she never gets the pleasure.' He smiled into her eyes, his outright laughter only just controlled. 'You say the most astounding things, Miss Rawson. My reputation is not at all secure with you around.'

'Nobody knows you're here.'

'You're doing it again,' he warned with amusement. 'I'm not sure whether it's plain old-fashioned innocence or deliberate misunderstanding.'

That remark made sure that she escorted him to the hall very warily, and it was stepping out into the hall after the cosy evening by the fire that brought back the earlier fears. Her eyes looked round a little anxiously and she hastily tried to smile.

'I tested the door as I went for the pizza,' he assured her quietly. 'In any case, they'll have forgotten about you by now.' She couldn't bring herself to agree and he took her shoulders in strong hands and looked down at her. 'I could put you into one of the hotels for tonight,' he offered, but she shook her head, her eyes never leaving his face, scared how she would feel as he left.

'I'll be fine, really.'

'Then don't look at me like that,' he ordered softly. 'I'm perfectly well aware that you need someone here with you all night. It's also obvious that you don't want Hart here. I could offer to sleep on your settee, but I'm not going to.'

'I don't want you to,' Tamara whispered, looking hastily away from those dark eyes that watched her intently.

'You do,' he corrected quietly. 'Normally I would be happy to oblige, but not with you.'

She looked at him miserably. This evening she had felt
close to him, and now he was saying that...

'I doubt if I would stay in my own bed,' he went on
softly as he saw the misunderstanding. 'I'm a perfectly
normal male, worse than most probably. I want to make
love to you, gently, slowly and for a very long time.
You've already had very unseemly male attention tonight, if those youths can be given that name, and fur-
thermore you're much too young for complications.'

'I—I wouldn't...' Tamara began desperately, utterly
shocked at this admission, but he tilted her flushed face
and looked at her deeply, his eyes running along the de-
fenceless trembling of her mouth.

'You would. We definitely have an effect on each
other,' he assured her quietly. 'Goodnight, Tamara.'

He suddenly bent his dark head and kissed her gently,
lingering on her soft lips when she made no move to
resist. For a second he pulled her closer and it was
frightening how she wanted more, how she felt quite
bereft when he put her firmly away and walked to the
door.

'Lock up and go to bed,' he advised. 'By tomorrow
this will all seem quite unlikely and, in any case, you'll
have your temper back.'

Somehow she didn't think so. She locked the door
carefully and then walked back to the remains of the
fire, clearing away the plates, feeling almost unreal.
There was a terrible feeling that she had missed something very important in life. It wasn't the first time she
had been kissed, even though she had been wary. Roger
kissed her goodnight every time he took her out. This,
though, was different. She was excited and scared all at
the same time, as if she had wanted to step off a cliff
and lacked the nerve.

No. She hadn't lacked the nerve—she had been too bemused to think about caution. She had been firmly pushed back. She stood and looked at herself in the mirror and she couldn't see anything wrong with being twenty-four. It wasn't too young for anything at all. In any case, she had only wanted him to stay around a while longer. And she hadn't looked at him in any other way. She was sure she hadn't.

In future she must be very careful to avoid him because he obviously had the idea that women ran after him. They probably did, she mused. He was handsome, rich, but more than that there was a sort of controlled sensuality about him that would set any woman's heart racing. She would ring him up and thank him quite coolly, and then she would keep out of his way altogether.

She slept well; a brandy and two glasses of wine helped a lot when normally she never drank more than one glass of white wine with a meal, and only if she was out even then. The thought of her ordeal was never in her mind, the rough youths almost forgotten. It was Jason's dark face that lingered. Maybe he *was* a noble savage, she mused as she drifted to sleep. After all, he had protected her. When she thought about what he had finally said she felt a burst of unwanted excitement until she realised it was probably all not true, just a sure-fire way of making an exit. He would be good at that. She wondered how he got out of boring business meetings. He couldn't use the same line then. Her last thought was that she was probably almost drunk and wandering in her mind.

She kept to her plan and rang the next day, but he wasn't there at all. Miss Phillips told her quite sadly that Mr Tysak had flown to Paris that very morning. He had a close friend there. It all slipped out before she pulled herself up smartly and became businesslike again.

'I'll make a note that you called, Miss Rawson.'

'Please don't,' Tamara said briskly. 'It was nothing important. A very small thing actually. I'll ring again when he comes back.'

Paris. He probably had a woman there, Tamara mused. Somebody over thirty, sophisticated, worldly-wise and glittering. Certainly not somebody who stupidly got herself attacked and ended up looking dreadful, with a well-scrubbed face and a thick dressing-gown. Certainly not someone who burst into tears and said embarrassing things.

Anyway, it didn't matter, she told herself firmly. There was the fashion show to organise and it was creeping up fast. This year Edwina wanted to show swimwear too. It would make for a very good show. They would have all their things on display and they always had a full house. She went headlong into work and Jason went right to the back of her mind, where he belonged. The fight was over, as far as she was concerned, and she didn't have to have anything more to do with him except as a tenant. A cool, polite tenant, that was what she would be.

CHAPTER FIVE

On Monday a weak and watery sun shone, and as
Tamara pulled up and looked across to the mews she
had the decided feeling that something was wrong. The
small fault in her car had been dealt with efficiently by
the garage and she sat for a moment and let her eyes
range over the mews, puzzling about the feeling that
bubbled up inside. It almost seemed like another place.
What was it?

Then she had it! There were no workmen, no hammering, no banging, no music. The Old Manor Hotel
stood there as if it had been discarded. It was surprising
what a pang it gave her. She had grown used to the work
without even knowing it, and since the night when Jason
had rescued her she had even smiled at the men on her
way across the park. They were not there, and it most
certainly was not a public holiday.

When she got into the shop the urge to ring Jason's
office and enquire was tremendous, but she contained
it. It was nothing to do with her. She hadn't set eyes on
him. As far as she knew, he was still in Paris. His rescue
and kindness had been just a chance thing. What he did
with his property was none of her business.

Trade was slack that day and it was Janet's day off.
It wasn't until she was having dinner with Roger that
night that she discovered anything at all.

'Going to the meeting tomorrow night?' he asked in
a suspiciously casual voice. It seemed to Tamara that he
had been behaving oddly since he had called for her, and

she glanced across quickly, surprising a rather tight look
on his face.

'What meeting?'

'I often wonder if you live in the same world as other
people,' he mocked a little crossly. 'There have been
notices stuck on almost every wall and telegraph pole in
town.'

'I—I haven't really been out. Anyway, I never saw
any.' Tamara felt her face flush a little. She had stayed
in each evening for two reasons. One, she hadn't quite
got over the mean little attack on her by the youths, and
two, she had hoped without admitting it that Jason would
call. Naturally he hadn't. He might be still in Paris or
he might be back, she didn't know. And why should he
call her anyway? 'What notices?' she enquired firmly,
pulling herself together. 'And what meeting?'

'There's a public meeting tomorrow night at seven—
town hall,' Roger enlightened her. 'It's about Lancrest
Mews.'

Cold washed over Tamara's skin. A lot of things had
happened since she had instigated the revolt. Jason had
forgiven her, they were almost certainly secure with their
leases and, as far as she knew, Mrs Prost and her ladies
had been satisfied. Anyhow, Jason had rescued her,
kissed her. She felt differently. It couldn't still be going
on!

'But why?' She stared anxiously at Roger and he
looked a little annoyed at her lack of enthusiasm.

'If you remember, I wrote an article about our
Edwardian heritage. Also, if you recall, those leaflets
invited people to batter away at the council. Well, apparently they did. Those who represent us have thought
it necessary to calm us down.'

'But everything *is* calmed down,' Tamara protested. 'We've even had the windows double-glazed and the doors fixed to stop dust.'

'The original source of discontent was what is happening to Lancrest Mews, if you recall,' Roger reminded her coolly. 'It was the future you had in mind, surely?'

'Well, I—I'm satisfied,' Tamara muttered uneasily. Jason would blame her for this. Whatever happened, it all came back to her, back to the original declaration of war.

'Could that be anything to do with the fact that he spent a long time at your flat the other night?'

So that was it! That was the reason for Roger's tight expression, his cool manner.

'He took me home,' she agreed firmly. 'I was attacked.'

'Really? And I thought he was such a sophisticated chap. You mean, you resisted?'

'You can just stop that!' Tamara said heatedly. 'Some youths attacked me and he just happened to be passing. He drove me home and saw to it that I was all right.'

'A lengthy job,' Roger pointed out grimly. 'According to our photographer who lives in a flat across the road, that great shining Jaguar was there for all of four hours.'

'We had a meal,' Tamara snapped, seething with annoyance. 'I was scared to be alone, and you can tell your photographer to mind his own business!'

'If you were scared, why didn't you ring me?' Roger asked angrily. 'I would have been round at once. To have the paper's photographer inform me that my girl has been alone in her flat with another man for four hours is not the best way to win my undying gratitude.'

'Then sack him!' Tamara raged, furious that she had to keep her voice down. 'And I'm just a friend of yours.'

'A girlfriend! And a lot more too if I hadn't been giving you plenty of loose rein.'

'End of friendship!' Tamara announced, beginning to stand, her amber eyes flashing sparks. Roger's hand on her arm stayed her action and his eyes were looking towards the door, not at her.

'Make your mind up about that in a few minutes,' he warned sarcastically. 'Here's your hero with his heroine.'

She dared not look round. If Jason was here he would probably stalk across and give her a piece of his mind. He hadn't been at all wary of doing that in public before. He had stormed into Impressions twice with no thought at all about any observers, and that had only been when the paper and then the leaflets had come out. What would he do about a meeting, a public meeting?

She subsided reluctantly and after a second risked a glance in his direction. She was stunned at the effect of that glance. She felt her own face stiffen with shock. Jason was with a very beautiful woman. They were sitting right across the room but the glamour seemed to reach out everywhere.

He was an arresting man at any time but tonight he looked even more so, darkly masculine, his face softened, almost openly sensuous, and small wonder with that woman breathing all over him, Tamara thought. She must be in her mid-thirties, sure of herself, wonderfully dressed in what Tamara recognised at once as designer clothes. Her sleek black hair caught the lights, and Jason was giving her his total attention. Somehow she had never thought of seeing him with a woman. If he was to live here in the same town she knew she would have to face that. Until now it had not been something she would have thought at all worrying.

She was reminded that he had twice told her she was too young. This was why, and it was clear that she had been right too. The murmur about wanting to make love to her had been as she had suspected—a good excuse to leave. She felt foolish, definitely weepy and terribly let down.

She fought the feeling, telling herself not to be ridiculous. Here was a wealthy, sophisticated man with his lady-love. He had merely rescued an acquaintance from trouble when he had helped her. He had stayed because he was kind. He was nothing to do with her at all.

'Don't take it too hard,' Roger advised, his hand covering hers. 'Just note and take warning. He's out of our class, Tamara, love. He moves in different circles.'

'I don't exactly know why you're giving such grandfatherly advice,' Tamara said briskly, catching her wandering feeling firmly back, forcing herself to acknowledge the advice inside her head even if she would not tell Roger about it. 'I told you, he rescued me. It was good of him, considering the way I've harassed him about the mews. I was in a state and he stayed a while.'

'I'll forgive you,' Roger said infuriatingly, as if she needed any forgiveness at all. 'Now finish your meal and we'll go.'

She tried, but suddenly she wasn't hungry any more, and when she glanced up again Jason was looking across, his face like dark ice as she gave a tentative smile. The friendly gesture was certainly not returned and her heart sank like lead. He knew about the meeting. She was knee-deep in trouble again. She carefully didn't look across as they left, and she was grateful when Roger's arm came around her waist in a very proprietorial manner.

She reviewed that gratitude later as Roger kissed her goodnight. He was extremely heated and she had to pull

away urgently after a second, looking at him almost with
alarm.

'I don't want to be your friend any more, Tamara,'
he said unevenly. 'It's time we were much more than
that.'

'Are you proposing?' she asked, trying to be light
about it. She had felt no tendency to linger in his arms
at all, and her mind had been doing a lot of comparing;
it just wouldn't stop doing it.

'When I can afford you,' he assured her with a sudden
grin. 'Meanwhile there's a lot of pleasure and we're both
missing it.'

He helped her out of the car and showed every intention of going into her flat with her. She clutched her
bag tightly, having no inclination at all to hand it over,
as she had done with Jason. She knew what would
happen as soon as they were safely indoors. Safety would
not be on the agenda, not for her.

'Thank you for dinner,' she said demurely. 'I'll ring
you tomorrow.'

'So I don't get invited in like Tysak?' He sounded
angry again, and Tamara looked straight at him.

'I explained all that. I didn't have to, you know. I'm
a free agent. You can tell your snoopy photographer that
he missed a scoop—local shopkeeper mugged. No doubt
he's snooping now, and I do not intend to give him any
more cause for speculation. If he continues I might just
sue him!'

He knew Tamara's temper and he calmed down, his
normal grin back in place.

'I'll have great pleasure in telling him.' He gave a laugh
and kissed her cheek. 'Forgive the heat. You're a
beautiful girl, Tamara.'

That's what Jason had said, she mused as she went into her flat. She gazed at herself in the nearest mirror. She wasn't into comparing beauty but she knew glamour and sophistication when she saw it. Should she keep up her modelling look? she wondered, her head on one side as she contemplated her reflection. All she did nowadays was try to look ordinary, but she had not been away from the modelling world for very long, after all. She had all the tricks at her fingertips.

She walked into her bedroom angrily, tossing off her coat. What was she proposing to do, run after Jason Tysak? Anyway, her mind pointed out cautiously, he would soon be on the warpath. If his icy looks tonight were anything to go by he was back to contemplating retaliation.

He did nothing. If she hadn't seen him with her own eyes she would have imagined he was still out of the country. She heard about the meeting from one of Mrs Prost's friends. Local concern had been stirred up so much that work had been temporarily stopped on everything.

'But he already has permission,' Tamara said in amazement.

'The concern is about the mews, not the hotel. As to stopping work on the hotel, he's done that himself. Apparently he's doing nothing else until this is sorted out.'

His reputation, Tamara realised. His firm was all-important to him. Rather than lose its reputation he would knock down the Old Manor Hotel, build another strip of park, leave the district and write it all off to experience. It brought on a surprising attack of gloom.

'What about us?' Edwina wanted to know when this was passed on to her later.

'I don't know. I don't want to know and I refuse to think about it,' Tamara stated emphatically. 'I'm doing the fashion show and then I'm going to live day by day. After the show I'm going home to tell my mother,' she added darkly, making Edwina laugh.

It wasn't so damned funny, Tamara mused. Right now she wanted to escape to comfort because her world was not now so clear cut as it had been. The fact that Jason had done nothing at all made each day an anxious occasion. She could have coped better with a wild row, a stormy scene, a heated battle. Being ignored was both hurtful and worrying—as it was Jason Tysak who was doing it. He was probably sitting in his office with a dark, stiff face and narrowed eyes, planning silently— like a war chief.

The fashion show was held each year at the local secondary school. It had everything there that was needed and after original misgivings Tamara had accepted it and had kept to the same venue each year.

It was a new building in well-kept grounds, had plenty of parking space, and the changing-rooms in the gym made good changing-rooms for the girls. Not that they had time to go into them! Once started it was fast and furious, with plenty of volunteers for dressers. The stage of the school was pretty much perfect, and the local carpenter had made an impromptu catwalk that stretched out into the audience.

The show was always packed out and this year was no exception, in spite of the wet weather. Tamara peeped out from behind the curtains and cast an eye over the murmuring audience. Plenty of clients there. The old ones preening as if it were especially for them and quite a few new possibilities, by the look of it. There were not many seats left and she knew that before the show started people would be standing at the back.

It was always a success and gave her a great deal of pleasure each year, apart from the custom it brought. Since she had started it and Impressions, the trade at the other mews shops had doubled. She went back to. see that everything was going well.

She and Janet had been here since early afternoon, putting the clothes out for each model. Edwina had come along later with her own things and so had Kenneth Dennison, his shoes stacked in boxes by each place. The girls had all been given free hair-dos by Eric and it looked like being a very professional, glittering show.

'I'll give them a bit of background music.' The man who did their music each year looked at Tamara enquiringly and she nodded. There was only one person missing, and Tamara's head rose expectantly as Mrs Prost came in, quite flustered and alone. Not again!

'Oh, Tamara! I'm so sorry. Gillian has one of her headaches. She just can't make it tonight but I came anyway to help with the dressing.'

'Why do we bother with that wretched girl?' Janet muttered. 'This is the second time she's let us down in three shows. Twice in a row too. She did this at the autumn show, and I know perfectly well it was because of that party at the tennis club.'

'We'll have to manage,' Tamara said rapidly before Mrs Prost saw Janet's annoyed looks. 'We'll spread the clothes out. If each girl does one extra outfit...'

'We'll have pandemonium!' Edwina finished. 'They're all arranged for colouring and height.'

'Then let's get cracking!' Tamara started to move clothes and Janet joined in grumpily. Mrs Prost actually looked uncomfortable and it served her right, Tamara

mused. She knew perfectly well how unreliable Gillian
was.

'This is the very last time,' she murmured to Janet.

'I'll keep you to that. Jane will have to wear a size
twelve. I'll pin her into it.'

It was all pretty hectic, but when the music for the
start of the show struck up they were all ready, the local
girls being hushed severely by Edwina, the professional
models enjoying themselves enormously. And the place
was now jam-packed full. Tamara peeped once again
through the curtains, watching the girls move on to the
stage, her eyes critical but pleased as they walked down
the catwalk and turned at the end. Pretty good!

Suddenly her face froze. He was there, right by the
edge of the catwalk, that woman with him. What was
Jason doing here? For a wild minute she thought he had
come to get his own back, to wreck her show, but
common sense told her he would do no such thing. He
was too wealthy, too sophisticated and quite above spite.
Maybe they hadn't had anything to do this evening?

The thought of them both at Jason's house made her
inexplicably miserable, and she didn't look again.

'This is probably the best show we've done yet!' Janet
exclaimed enthusiastically, rushing in and getting down
to helping her own particular girl change fast. 'What's
next?'

'The pink suit.' Tamara glanced at her clipboard and
turned away, too busy to linger.

'What about the swimwear in the finale?' Edwina
asked in a frosty voice. 'How can anyone double up for
Miss Gillian Prost then?'

'But surely?' Mrs Prost had the grace to blush and
Tamara looked uneasy as it dawned on her. Gillian was
supposed to wear Edwina's *pièce de résistance*, two

hundred pounds' worth of next to nothing with a wrap. Every single girl had a suit to wear. Nobody could double up.

'What do I do?' Edwina persisted crossly. 'Do I go out and just hold it up?'

She was very annoyed, and Tamara could see another battle beginning as Mrs Prost's face reddened further. Also she didn't have either the nerve or the cruelty to tell Edwina to leave it out. It was a really wondrous creation, sure to bring custom.

'Why don't you wear it, Tamara?' one of the dressers said, and Tamara looked at her, open-mouthed.

'I'm not a model.'

'You could walk right back into a job in London any time you wanted,' one of the London girls said wryly, and everyone just stopped and looked at Tamara expectantly.

She would have said yes with no further thought, but Jason was out there. He made her shake at the knees, and there was that woman with him. It was thinking of the woman that brought her out of her nervous dither. It was sheer madness! She didn't really know him at all. She was behaving like a fool, like a nervous teenager.

'Fine. I'll do it.' It sounded like somebody else's voice, and later she wished it had been.

It was to be the very last item. Gillian had been supposed to enter as all the other models stood at the side and posed. Just the sort of thing Mrs Prost had wanted, but it was plain to see that Gillian had not got her mother's nerve. Tamara decided to have a long motherly talk with Gillian the next time she got her to herself.

She had to borrow somebody else's make-up case and it was only ease of long practice that had her ready in time, her hair swept up into a dark band, the wrap around her waist. The costume was eye-catching in more ways than one. Like the matching wrap, it was a swirl of vivid colour overlaid with silver roses, not the sort of thing she would have chosen herself. Without the wrap it was clinging, brief and high-legged.

Tamara lingered in the changing-room, her heart beating alarmingly. This was where she made a spectacle of herself. She was too old to do this sort of thing. It brought back Jason's words. According to him, she was too young. She could see quite plainly that she was some sort of misfit. Too old for glamour and too young for love. It annoyed her somewhat and gave her the courage to step out.

The London models whistled and grinned, and Tamara found herself smiling. She had enjoyed it down there. She should never have come here and tried her hand at business. It gave her something to ponder about and she waited for the music that would mark her entry without too many qualms.

The swimwear was greeted with wild applause and the noise calmed her even more. It was not until she heard her own cue that she felt anything at all. She had forgotten that particular music for a minute and she shouldn't have done that—*she* had chosen it, wickedly and wilfully. The final piece. It was not a strip-tease number but it sounded very much like it. The beat said it all, and now she was faced with her own little mischief.

'Here goes!' she muttered to Janet, and she felt just a little startled to see Edwina standing with her fingers crossed. Who did they think she was? Some idiot? She had been doing this since she was sixteen. She wasn't about to fall over her own feet!

She stepped out slowly, taking up the beat, and just for a moment she forgot that dark eyes would be watching her. She was back in the big fashion shows, the excitement of an audience, the music and the make-up all combining to send her far back into the past.

To say they were stunned was putting it mildly. Of course, they all recognised her. She was well known in town, well known for her smart clothes, her quiet, demure air, a local businesswoman. Now they were looking at something quite different. Her sheer beauty, her professional gloss and her deliberately sexy walk stunned them.

In the middle of the catwalk she discarded the wrap with a swirl of movement, and then the applause came *and* the whistles. It didn't bother her at all. She was enjoying herself, playing a game, being defiant if she would have admitted it. She followed it through to the end, coming back to the stage where the models were actually applauding too and then walking back, swinging the gauzy wrap.

Roger stood up in the audience, clapping wildly, and she flashed him a very professional smile. It was only then that she looked at Jason as he sat almost beside her and the devil really got into her at the look on his face. Far from being captivated, he disapproved! He had a look on his face that assured her he would have liked to shake her. The cheek of it stunned her, but only for a second. If he was trying to humiliate her he was backing the wrong horse. She paused deliberately and winked at him openly and slowly. That almost brought the house down.

She was glad to get off then. Edwina wanted to smother her in kisses but she escaped, muttering about the small cocktail party that always followed the evening's show. In fact, she just wanted to lock the cubicle door and recover. The wink had been just too much and she knew it. Jason had looked at her intently, a grim smile growing on his face. His looks had threatened retaliation—sexual retaliation. He had not looked kind and considerate either and she knew she had embarrassed him.

Tamara altered her make-up, toning it down, brushed her hair back to her shoulders and put on her dress. Somehow she knew he would be at the party. He had been sitting in a reserved seat. Those seats paid more and they also paid for the party. It was all for charity, the hospital and the school. She tried to hang back, but it was impossible.

'Get over to the party,' the helpers insisted, backed roundly by Janet. 'We'll clear up. You can't be late— it's mostly your affair.'

Well, it was Edwina's and Kenneth's and Eric's too, but nobody seemed to notice that each year. It was called the Impressions Show and she knew perfectly well she had to turn up at the hotel close by. Everything was laid on for them. She had never wanted to duck out before. But then, she had never deliberately tried to provoke a man before. It would have been wise not to pick on Jason! She admitted to being scared.

The private room at the King's Head was already crowded when Tamara arrived, and she tried to slip in unnoticed. There wasn't a lot of chance of that. Her entrance was marked by clapping and a few wild cheers. She couldn't have been more noticeable if she had come in the swimsuit.

It was a relief to chatter to people she knew, and Roger joined them almost immediately, a look in his eyes that had never been there before.

'So that's what you did in London!' he murmured, slipping his arm round her. 'It's a good job you're already my girl or I would be anxious.'

It was a bit too difficult to start stamping her foot and reminding him that she was no such thing, too many people were watching them, and she had to smile sweetly and put up with it. And she hadn't done that sort of thing in London either. She had always refused to do swimwear and undies.

Jason, she noted, was at the other side of the room, ignoring her. This evening his lady-love was in black and it suited her enormously, a silk wrap-over dress that cleverly clung to her figure. Once again Tamara was forced to admit to the other woman's sophistication. She looked like somebody who would travel the world with ease and not one qualm of worry. Her jewellery was fabulous.

Jason looked across as if he was reading her mind, and he wasn't one bit amused either. He had a way of standing out from a crowd, a dangerous way. He wasn't scowling; he didn't have to. His disapproval was just icily cold. She couldn't seem to stop staring at him and finally he nodded to her, raising his glass almost insolently, making her colour deepen. She felt ashamed of her little trick at the show. In fact, she felt quite cheap, as if she had been trying to provoke him.

'I could have died when you winked at Jason Tysak at the show,' one of her influential customers said with a bubbly laugh as she came up. Tamara could have died too—gladly. She just hoped he couldn't hear that fruity, over-loud voice. 'Imagine! After all the trouble he's caused you, Tamara. It was quite naughty. Really sexy.'

Didn't she just know it? It had seemed like a good idea at the time but now it just seemed to be madness.

Jason Tysak was a man to avoid, not provoke. Anyone with even an ounce of sense would barricade the doors if he was near by.

Roger apparently saw things from another angle entirely—his own male standing.

'You did what?' he muttered angrily as the woman moved away. 'Am I hearing things? You actually winked at Tysak in front of all those people? What did he do, signal back that he'd be round at your flat later?'

Tamara's cheeks were glowing hot, embarrassment and temper making a very volatile cocktail, much more potent than anything at the bar.

'It was part of the act and he just happened to be there,' she snapped in a low, angry voice.

'Just as he happened to be passing as you were supposedly attacked, and just as he happened to stay for four hours?' Roger gritted in a savagely low voice too.

'I am not your property!' Tamara stated angrily. 'Believe what you want to believe. If our friendship is to continue then just back off!'

He turned away and strode out of the room, obviously furious, and several eyes followed him before coming back to Tamara.

She had the terrible feeling that they knew—at least, they knew some of it—and by tomorrow morning the episode of the wink would be all over town. They gossiped in this town, and she should know—hadn't she made good use of that when her campaign had started? Now it was backfiring at great speed. How to make a fool of yourself without really trying!

She still hadn't got herself perfectly under control when a hand came to her elbow and she was being ushered firmly to the edge of the bar, where there was a small quiet spot in the middle of turmoil.

'I can see he didn't like it,' Jason murmured almost in her ear. He handed her another drink and she stared at him blankly, willing her face to remain unflustered and stay a normal colour.

'Who didn't like what?' she enquired with a great deal of poise.

'Your boyfriend didn't like the nice, sexy wink,' he stated unhesitatingly. 'I saw him go off raging.'

'You're not as observant as I had imagined,' Tamara managed with a cool little smile. 'Roger was annoyed about having to leave. He had a lead to follow up. Journalism is pretty demanding, you know.'

'Well, I could see him demanding explanations,' Jason murmured sardonically. 'How did you wriggle out of it?'

'There was nothing to wriggle out of!' Tamara snapped, turning on him furiously. 'The wink was part of the act. You just happened to put your face in the way.'

'Really?' He gave her a derisive look. 'Am I to understand that it could have landed almost anywhere? If the young Miss Prost hadn't failed you, as I am informed, and forced you to take part, would she have delivered the provoking little signal? I can't see her mother allowing that.'

'You don't know anything about anything!' Tamara seethed, losing the battle with her blushes. He knew perfectly well why she had done it, she could tell that.

'I know an invitation when I see one. I realised I was being invited to stay the other night too. Of course, then I never looked further than your beautiful face. I now appreciate you a little more. I also begin to understand that you're not the lovely, bewildered innocent with the unreliable temper I thought you were. State your terms,

Tamara, but don't expect to marry a millionaire, will you? It will be just a sleeping partnership.'

She tossed her drink right over him and she didn't care who saw. It was all too fast for him to retaliate and she stormed across the room and out into the darkness without looking back. If anyone dared attack her tonight she would kill them on the spot.

All she could hear was the beat of temper in her head and the angry clicking of her heels, but as she came to her car she suddenly realised that there were other footsteps behind her, sounding as angry as her own. Before she could open the car door strong hands gripped her and she was spun round as Jason towered over her furiously.

'It's not as easy as that to dispatch me, you little red-haired cat!' he grated.

'Let me go!' Tamara struggled but he simply pushed her against the car, holding her fast.

'Oh, no,' he muttered angrily. 'There's action and reaction in everything, and nobody does that to me!'

'Nobody speaks like that to me either!' Tamara raged.

'You mean I mistook your intentions? There was no invitation?'

He was scathing, looking at her as if she were an awful person, and she had only anger to protect herself from that look. She tried to lash out at him but he only moved closer until she was trapped between the car and the hard, uncompromising body.

'Your girlfriend will come looking for you,' she scorned.

'Let her,' he jeered. 'She's only a part-time occupation with me and she knows it.' His grip tightened to cruelty. 'Talk is over, Miss Rawson.'

His lips burned into hers, punishing and hard, stopping her breath, and struggling was out of the question. Tamara's mind raced frantically and every action was instinctive. She just stood there and accepted it, her body like wood, her mind frozen against him, the only escape she had.

He lifted his head and looked down at her, seeing her blank face and the subdued pain in eyes that had never closed. His own anger seemed to die right then, and he let his shoulders relax from tight annoyance.

'Why did you do it?' he muttered frustratedly. 'Why did you walk like that, wink like that? Don't you know what it looked like?'

Tamara was incapable of answering. Suddenly she just wanted to cry, to crawl away, and his hand softened.

'Oh, Tamara,' he murmured. 'You're a crazy girl.' His hand came to stroke back her hair, and when she still stood stiffly he cupped her face and let his lips drift over hers. 'I'm not going to hurt you,' he assured her softly. He parted her lips with slow insistence, his hand stroking her face, and when she began to soften from her frozen state he turned her until he leaned against the car and she was pulled against his warmth.

CHAPTER SIX

IT ALL began slowly, almost as if it was an apology for Jason's savage attack. Tamara needed comfort and he was giving it, but before long the same feeling came back inside her, the glow of heat in her stomach, the trembling in her legs, and comfort gave way to something entirely different as his lips demanded more and the kiss deepened.

She was shocked when his tongue began to probe her lips, running along the soft, swollen contours, and as she gasped his tongue slid inside her mouth, urgently exploring until she shivered in his arms and gripped his shoulders desperately. He ran his hand down her spine, compelling her closer, his legs parting to bring her against him, and she felt the hard arousal of his body for the first time, her own body responding achingly.

His stroking hands moved over her, discovering the tight, swollen evidence of her breast, and he lifted his head, his dark eyes searching her face as his hand slid into the opening of her dress.

'No!' She tried to move, instinct warning her to put him as far away as possible.

'Yes, Tamara,' he breathed, ignoring her pleas and taking her lips with his as his hand moved possessively to cover her breast. It was heavy, silken, surging to fill his palm, even though she tried to control the desire that came in a wild rush.

99

'Please! Please don't,' she whispered shakily, her head moving from side to side in torment, trying to escape his lips. 'People——'

'Come with me, then,' he demanded thickly. 'Leave your car and get into mine. Come back home with me. I want you.'

'No!' She struggled against the hand that stroked her but his arm was like iron, refusing to let her go. 'What will you tell that woman?' she asked bitterly, making herself cling to reality as his thumb rubbed softly over her nipple.

'The hell with her,' he said frustratedly. 'I want *you*.'

It brought her back to earth. What was she doing, letting him touch her, letting him make suggestions like that? She didn't know him and he was treating her as if she were cheap, willing. He would no doubt say the same thing about her later.

It brought back the frozen stiffness and she jerked free violently.

'Don't touch me!' she ordered sharply as he reached for her. 'Let me into my car or I'll go back inside and ask for protection.'

'Protection? From me?' His expression was stunned, as if she were a possession he could collect when he felt like it.

'I don't know you,' she said tightly. 'I don't want to know you. You're the enemy. You rescued me from an attack, but what are you doing now but attacking me? That makes us even.'

'Tamara!' He moved towards her but she backed off, staring at him bitterly, and he suddenly turned, his face pale and cold as he walked back towards the party.

She trembled all the way back to her flat, tears of humiliation on her face. Men! How wise she had been to steer clear of them so far. Roger had a chauvinistic chip on his shoulder, and, as to Jason Tysak, he was a monster! Who did he think he was, acting as if he owned her, making demands that just showed his opinion of her? For two pins she would start the battle about the mews all over again. If he ever needed her mercy it would not be forthcoming. She would see him fall by the wayside and laugh in his face.

Rage and humiliation had turned to trembling misery by the time she got home. Whoever had won this latest battle, it certainly had not been her. She wasn't quite sure what had happened to her lately but she wasn't the same person. Once she had been dignified and cool, a successful model and then a rising business lady. Now she was a virago with a tendency to act badly without warning. She was also a person who let Jason hold her whenever he felt like it.

She locked herself in and stood under the shower later, fighting off tears. He had made her feel more cheap than ever. He had stormed after her to punish her and then had thought of a better way, and she had let him. She tried not to think of the desire that had surged through him, through both of them. It was best forgotten; so was the look in his eyes as he had walked away.

Maybe he wouldn't let them stay now? In four days the leases were due to be signed. She had humiliated him in front of everyone. It would all be held against her and nobody knew what he had done to her. She certainly wasn't about to enlighten them either. Once again Jason had won.

The phone rang and she hoped it wasn't Roger, because she couldn't cope tonight. She had to answer because it just might be her mother, but she picked it up very cautiously.

'Hello?' She hadn't expected to put quite so much caution into her enquiry and when her name was spoken firmly in a very masculine voice she squeezed herself back into the cushions in an attitude of retreat that would have startled anyone who knew her.

'Tamara?' When she didn't answer he spoke more firmly still. 'All right. If you don't want to answer I can understand, but please listen at least. I'm sorry. Did you hear that?'

It couldn't be Jason apologising, surely? She just sat there silently.

'I knew perfectly well that the wink was part of the act and I accept that I put my face in the way, as you pointed out so amusingly,' he went on, ignoring her silence. 'I had no business to speak to you as I did or act as I did. I can only offer the excuse that you have an unfailing ability to infuriate me. It's almost a gift, in fact. When I get my hands on you I'm sorry to say that things seem to slip out of my control.'

'I—I'm *not* running after you!' Tamara ventured into small indignant sound. 'I'm not accustomed to being insulted.'

'You retaliated quite perfectly,' he assured her wryly. 'And would you be interested to know that I have a cherry in my breast pocket?' Tamara felt an attack of giggles coming on, but she refused to let them because she was sure it was hysteria and she was not going to lower her dignity now that she had it back. 'Next time I'll see that you get a lemonade only,' he added. 'No cocktails.'

'There won't be a next time,' Tamara said. And why did she think she had her dignity back just because he was talking to her? The world did not revolve around Jason Tysak and she wasn't going to start thinking it did. 'We're worlds apart, Mr Tysak, and obviously that's a good arrangement. In all probability we shall never meet again.'

'I know,' he agreed quietly. 'That's why I wanted to apologise. I don't like leaving on a sour note. Goodnight, Tamara. I've enjoyed our clashes. I'll remember you as an unusual opponent. And Tamara, you're beautiful.'

He rang off, and Tamara was a few minutes before she put the phone down. It was as if a door had closed in her life. Nothing exciting would happen again in this town after he left, and clearly he was leaving. Maybe he hadn't bought a house after all. Maybe he had only been thinking about it and the trouble had made him reconsider—the trouble she had caused.

She had another attack of gloom and went to bed feeling quite lonely. It was the end of an era. It showed exactly what sort of a town this was because take Jason away and there was about as much life here as there was on a bare mountain. She wasn't humiliated now. She only remembered the sheer bliss of it, the kisses, his skilled hands. She had probably been too sheltered if she had lived for almost twenty-five years and never felt that before.

The doorbell rang the next morning before Tamara was even dressed. When she answered it reluctantly she was shaken to find Jason standing there, looking immaculate. At the moment it wasn't raining but there was a great deal of heavy cloud in the sky, and with the background of this darkness he looked astonishingly masculine and virile. He had a grey jacket on with dark trousers and a casual shirt that might well have cost a fortune.

'What do you want?' She stared at him solemnly, keenly conscious of the mess she looked in her old blue dressing-gown.

'It's Saturday,' he pointed out drily.

'I can't see anything exciting in that statement,' Tamara assured him tightly, wanting to shut the door and hide. 'I've known other Saturdays. They come each week and I get to lie in bed and have some sleep.'

'I'm taking you out,' he stated firmly, and she looked at him warily, not about to fall for another thing. She had worked hard on her character during the night, and this morning she felt much better, as if she had rid herself of a whole lot of nonsense. He was part of it.

'You can't be drunk because it's too early,' she said bleakly. 'It must therefore be some sort of reprisal you're planning because of the drink episode last night. I'm too much on guard, Mr Tysak. You've changed my character. I'm cautious now, so, whatever it is, forget it, and I most certainly do not want to see you again.'

'It's all for business. I planned a trip,' he assured her seriously.

'I'm glad. Enjoy it. Send me a postcard.'

'Tamara!' He looked at her in amused exasperation. 'You're keeping me standing on the step. People don't usually treat me like that.'

'They'll learn,' she muttered, her hand firmly on the door. 'I've learned quickly and I'll let you into a secret. Across the road in one of the flats there's a photographer. He works for the local paper and he snoops. He snooped the other night when you brought me home and stayed for four hours. I didn't even know that myself but he clocked it all up on the old stop-watch. Luckily we were outside the range of his telescope last night but he's probably at the window now, making brief but accurate notes. Wild horses wouldn't get you in here.'

'I don't own any yet,' he countered. 'I'll do it all by myself.'

Before she could stop him he was inside the flat and had the door firmly closed, and Tamara turned on him angrily. She had not expected to see him again and she had herself all sorted out. Keeping away from him was essential. This was a violation of her rights.

'Go away!' she ordered furiously. 'You're a source of trouble, an endless pain in the neck. Go where you're going and leave me in peace. I will not discuss business or anything else with you.'

'I'm taking you out,' he stated emphatically. 'Get ready. What do you want for breakfast? Coffee and toast suit you?'

He was actually striding into her kitchen, and she scurried after him, breathlessly annoyed.

'Kindly leave my flat!' she commanded loudly. 'I did not invite you in and I'm ordering you to leave. I'll call the police!'

He just lifted her by the waist and sat her on the kitchen table, staring into her angry eyes with a great deal of determination.

'I'm going out and taking you with me,' he stated flatly. 'I want your help and you owe it to me to co-operate. I rescued you, but last night I forced my attentions on you. You said we were, therefore, even. We are not. Because of you I'm left with a half-finished hotel and an Edwardian mews I can well do without if it is to sit there unaltered. I need you on my side, and you're going to be on my side if I have to tie you up and dump you in the car. Now what do you want for breakfast? I haven't got all day.'

'I'll come,' Tamara stated mutinously, sliding from the table and edging past him. It would be safer in the car anyway. 'But I won't be on your side at all, not after last night. And I don't drink coffee at breakfast-time,' she added primly, 'it's bad for the digestion. I have orange juice, toast and tea.'

'Get dressed!' he ordered fiercely, glaring at her, and she rushed to comply but only, she told herself firmly, because he was big, a man and inclined to violence when crossed.

In view of his impeccable appearance, Tamara chose her clothes with care. She didn't know exactly what this was all about but she decided to be quite prepared for anything. She chose mid-blue trousers with a white silk shirt and topped it off with a fine wool jacket of dark biscuit colour. It suited, she decided after a critical look in the mirror.

When she arrived in the kitchen she was carefully made up and her honey-coloured hair was brushed and shining, left loose almost to her shoulders. Jason's eyes ran over her and he frowned and pushed the toast forward irritably. He slammed the teapot on the table and set out two cups. Then he sat opposite, poured the tea and glared at her.

'I never asked to be bullied into a trip,' Tamara pointed out as she spread honey on the golden-brown toast. 'You thought all this up by yourself, so don't look so annoyed with me.' From now on she intended to keep him at arm's length. She hadn't expected to see him again and she had her mind all arranged carefully. Now he was upsetting things, but she wouldn't in any way soften up. With Jason it was too dangerous; he only had to touch her.

'You're the most irritating female I've ever known,' he informed her irascibly. 'Any other woman would have wanted to know where she was going.'

'But I don't care, do I?' Tamara reminded him, biting into her toast and looking resolutely away. 'I'm being forced into this expedition, but I don't have to like it.'

He didn't say anything else until she had finished her breakfast, which she did calmly and slowly. She was aware of his intent and irritated gaze all the time, but she never looked at him. She had every barrier up against him and they were going to remain up all day. Looking at him could only bring trouble. Those feelings would come back.

She put her cup and plate into the sink and walked away as she finished, and he stood up at once, clearly on guard.

'Where are you going?' He seemed to think that escape had entered her mind, and she smiled blankly at him.

'To clean my teeth. I was taught scrupulous dental hygiene from an early age. Old habits can't be broken.'

'Quite right,' he snapped. 'Hurry up. There's a long way to go.'

Even though she was dying to ask where, she desisted, and as they pulled away from her flat in the great shining Jaguar, no doubt observed by the man opposite, Tamara sank back into her seat and kept silent.

It was only as they left the town well behind that she found it impossible to keep quiet. It was darkly overcast in spite of the fact that it was nowhere near lunchtime, and it was surprisingly lonely when Jason sat grimly beside her and said nothing at all.

'You had no business to storm in and demand my co-operation!' she suddenly bit out into the silence. 'This is one of my free days. And another thing,' she added as he stared grimly ahead, 'you've now given that photographer more ammunition. You came very early and this car is particularly noticeable.'

'We have a long way to go,' he informed her stiffly. 'I have something to show you.'

'I won't look,' Tamara stated emphatically. 'I shall not look and I shall make no comment at all.'

His dark glance flashed across to her, racing over her face and hair.

'There is no real necessity to go on proving that you're alarmingly young,' he growled. 'Pretend a little sophistication until the expedition is over and I'll overlook your glaring faults.'

'I'm twenty-four, not fourteen!' Tamara seethed. 'I have one career behind me and another under way.'

'Then why behave like a spoiled brat?'

'It's you!' Tamara announced, turning sideways to glare. 'I object to your manner, your god-like belief in your own importance and your forceful way of insisting on being constantly in the right. I don't trust you one bit, and even a pig-headed man can't expect it after what you did.'

'It really is odd how you antagonise me,' he murmured ironically. 'I arrived at your door this morning with no thought of trouble. This could be a pleasant day but instead we're back to battle.'

'You made me come with you,' Tamara reminded him mutinously.

'You didn't kick and scream. Were you afraid of retaliation? Keep mentioning last night and I'll begin to think you liked it.' He was suddenly quietly sensuous, and Tamara felt her cheeks begin to glow. She did not need to be reminded about retaliation in a physical form from Jason.

'I was intrigued by your arrival this morning,' she assured him loftily. 'That's why I've come.'

'You will be intrigued,' he promised softly. 'I think you'll give careful consideration to my plans.'

'It's most unlikely,' Tamara said haughtily. 'And don't think you can either impress me or bully me.'

'I wouldn't even try,' he assured her, that wide grin back on his dark face. 'I know perfectly well that I have trouble sitting right beside me. I intend to proceed with caution. I'm even prepared to offer you a very splendid lunch.'

Tamara said nothing at all. She realised she would rather be fighting with Jason than not see him at all and it was worrying, very worrying.

'Do you float around in your dressing-gown when Hart calls?' he suddenly enquired harshly, his tone completely altered, and she turned on him at once. But her angry retort froze in her throat at the sombre look on his face.

'He rarely calls,' she confessed in a very matter-of-fact voice. 'Normally we meet to eat out. Sometimes we go to the theatre. On the odd occasion he has waited for me to get ready if I've been late. I don't recall floating at all.'

The look on his face had made her feel decidedly shaky and she dared not look at him again. He certainly wasn't interested in her, so it couldn't be jealousy. That being the case, it was most probably prying. She did some of her own.

'Is your lady-friend still staying with you?' she asked casually.

'Claire?' he said bleakly. 'She's back in Paris.'

So that was why he was round at the flat so early. He had nothing to do, so he had decided to work up some

action. Tamara felt bleak herself. He might not be
jealous, but she was. She admitted it. He was an exciting
man, and even though she raged at him every time they
met she couldn't forget the kisses and the warmth he had
shown when she needed him. She couldn't forget last
night either but she would take care not to mention it
again.

'OK,' she sighed. 'There's no need to sound so gloomy.
I expect she'll be back soon. In the meantime, I admit
that I owe you a favour for trouble caused by temper,
so, whatever it is, I promise to look and keep my childlike
comments to the very minimum. Trust in me.'

He started to laugh and the glance that flashed across
to her was lit by dark, dancing eyes.

'Oddly enough, you strange and bewildering female,
I *do* trust you,' he said quietly. 'That being the case, I'll
tell you why we're here and what you're going to see.'

It turned out to be a hotel. It was in a town just over
thirty miles north and the Jaguar flew along, eating up
the miles, making short work of the distance. Tamara
gazed around her. She had been contemplating coming
up here next weekend to see her mother and father, but
it looked very grim at the moment. On this main road
there was no flooding, but she could see it right across
the fields, many of them submerged in water.

'That's not just rain, you know,' she pointed out a
little worriedly. 'I heard that a couple of rivers have burst
their banks up here, and my mother told me that there's
still plenty of snow to melt.'

'Where do your parents live?' Jason glanced across
at the waterlogged fields and then ignored them. He
wasn't of the same nervous disposition, and Tamara tried
to put them out of her mind too.

'Further north by a long way—Cumbria. A little village into the hills. My father is a doctor, as I told you. His practice is mostly rural. Up there you have to watch the weather. It's another habit I haven't grown out of.'

They sped over a bridge and the river below was very high, right to the top of the bank. Pieces of branches and other bits of flotsam were racing along with the speed of the flow, and Tamara looked worriedly at Jason.

'You ought to take note of that,' she suggested. 'This is the main road. It won't take long for that to come over the top.'

'We really won't be all that long,' he said soothingly. 'A look over the hotel, lunch, and then we'll be on our way back. It will still be light.'

'Daylight won't help much if the road is flooded,' Tamara pointed out. 'We can watch each other drown, but apart from that it will be no help at all.'

'Shall we turn round and go back?' he asked, but she shook her head determinedly.

'No way! I'll chicken out when you do. Besides,' she added with a quick smile, 'I'm starving. Normally I eat twice as much breakfast.'

'I'll make a note of that fact.' He was smiling again and Tamara tried hard not to be pleased. She reminded herself forcefully that he was nothing to her at all. He was merely her new landlord, providing he renewed the leases. She kept quiet about that. They were due to be signed on Tuesday. She had the urge to ask while things were still pleasant, but she thought better of it. In the matter of the leases she would move with the others. She wouldn't let him think she was asking favours—he might demand some himself.

*   *   *

The hotel was Victorian, beautifully preserved, and there were Victorian shops too. In a way it was very much like Lancrest Mews but there were more shops. As it was Saturday, the streets were crowded, and after the car was parked Jason took her arm and led her to the nearest shop.

Outwardly they were all still from a bygone time, the façades beautifully kept, but inside they had been modernised to make life a little more easy than their first-time owners had found it.

He took her straight through the shop into the back, through a swinging glass door and out into what she had imagined would be the rear of the shop, Lancrest Mews being very much on her mind. It *was* the rear of the shop—there was a window there, showing the brightly lit interior—but there was no untidy yard, no sign of tacky additions to the original building as there was behind the four shops in the mews.

It was a covered arcade that led straight into the hotel and it brought business too, she could see that at once. Even now there were guests from the hotel coming into the arcade and going straight into the shops. There was no need whatever for them to face the bitterly cold air outside because it certainly was blowing out there.

She wandered off by herself, looking in each shop window from this angle, summing it all up and thinking about Lancrest Mews. When she walked back Jason was leaning against the hotel doorway, watching her. He seemed to have been talking to the manager, who left as she approached.

'Let's eat,' Jason suggested. 'You said you were hungry.'

She wasn't just hungry—she was stunned into silence. Was this what she had fought to ward off? It was wonderful, and she could see that her custom would grow beyond the people of the town. A big hotel like this would have plenty of guests, rich guests. In her imagination she could hear them saying, 'Let's go up to that old Edwardian hotel for the weekend. It's so luxurious, and we can shop at Impressions.'

She was sitting at a table and the meal had been ordered before she stopped dreaming about it. When she looked at Jason he was watching her intently, leaning back in his chair, looking very elegant and wealthy in this equally elegant hotel.

'Well, Tamara Rawson?' he prompted derisively.

'Is—is this what you intend to do with Lancrest Mews and the Old Manor Hotel?' she gulped.

He simply nodded and went on watching her. He didn't look at all angry and she was surprised he hadn't beaten her savagely before now. It was all so tasteful, so perfect.

'Did—did you get the idea from here?' she asked anxiously, wanting to keep him off the little matter of her interference for as long as possible.

'No. I've done this sort of thing in several places. Trying to keep traditional things is very important to me. In this particular place, though,' he added, looking round the really splendid dining-room, 'there were just the shops. Next to the shops was a large area of waste ground. We built this hotel from old plans, adding very modern facilities discreetly, of course.'

'This is a new hotel?' Tamara couldn't quite believe it.

'Brand-new,' he assured her. 'It's been open for about a year and a half and it's always booked up well in advance. I'm flattered that you can't tell the difference between this place and the shops.'

'So you own this hotel too?' Tamara asked sombrely, quite gloomy as she realised yet again his wealth and power. She was in another orbit, common or garden, ordinary, even if his intentions had been honourable.

'This and plenty more,' he agreed unconcernedly. 'Right now, though, I want to know how you feel about this being repeated in Lancrest Mews. The hotel being turned into Edwardian elegance, the shops being incorporated carefully, a covered parade at the back.'

'It's a wonderful idea,' she said almost tearfully. 'I'm sorry I fought it but you never came right out and stated your case.'

'I never got the chance, Tamara,' he reminded her. 'We had hardly started when I was in the middle of a battlefield, a wild opponent throwing spanners in the works.'

'I'll give it my backing,' she said hastily. 'I'll tell everybody, and I'll go to the council offices and back the plans.'

'Oh, there's not any difficulty there,' he assured her drily. 'The final plans are approved provisionally. All they're waiting for is peace and quiet. If we go ahead and this barrage of complaints continues it will really be too much effort to finish the thing off.'

'How can anyone complain about something like this?' Tamara asked.

'Well, you did,' he pointed out wryly. 'I offered to show you the plans the first time I saw you but you had some idea that the hotel would be actually run into the shops, the fronts of the shops plastered into the Old Manor Hotel and left with all the seams showing.'

'I didn't understand,' Tamara admitted, flushing miserably.

'As I recall, it was carved across your heart,' he reminded her.

'Sometimes I do things—impulsively,' she confessed.

'I know.' His voice was suddenly softened and when she looked up his eyes darkened even more and she knew he wasn't thinking about that drink episode, it was more her willingness to bury her head in his shoulder and cuddle against him thankfully. It was her willingness last night. 'Do I have a little co-operation in future, in the matter of Lancrest Mews?' he asked and she was glad to nod and look away.

'You can spy for me,' he ordered as they ate their meal. 'As I see it, this ladies' committee is responsible for a good deal of upheaval.'

'I put them up to it,' Tamara disclosed worriedly. 'I didn't say anything outright, you understand? I just— just acted gloomy and muttered and—and things like that. I never realised how far they would take it. I underestimated the power of somebody like Mrs Prost. In the end I was just swept aside and trampled on—in a manner of speaking.'

One black eyebrow was raised and his lips quirked several times, but he kept a straight face.

'Never mind,' he said quietly. 'We'll forget that. Now you're a double agent. I want to know everything they propose to do.'

'I couldn't do that, Jason!' Tamara put her fork down and looked quite shocked. 'That would be betrayal.'

'You let me know what they were about to do once before,' he pointed out.

'That was different,' she said earnestly. 'We didn't know that Mrs Prost was listening when we were talking about you, and I was scared that you would blame me and toss everyone out with me.'

'So you were pulling my character to pieces?' he asked quizzically. 'Think I won't toss you out now?'

'Will you?' She looked at him with enormous amber eyes and his glance softened from derision to warm amusement.

'No. I won't. In the meantime just watch out and at least let me know if there is anything startling about to happen. I've used up my quota of shocks with you. Any more and I'll just drop the whole project.'

'I'll see what I can do,' she promised quickly. She didn't want Jason to go away, she really didn't, ridiculous though it was.

'Then finish your meal and let's be going,' he said briskly, back to business at once.

But after the meal she wanted to browse through the shops and he had some things to talk over with the manager and, what with one thing and another, it was almost dark before they started their journey home. A very big mistake.

Initially Tamara was too busy thinking about the future appearance of Lancrest Mews, about Jason, who sat silently and drove, to give much thought to anything else. The threat of more rain had brought an early and gloomy dusk and she wanted to have time to think anyway, to sort out her feelings for this enigmatic man who seemed to have taken over her life to some extent. She never looked out really, never observed the outside world. Her own world was right here in the car beside Jason.

It was when he suddenly braked sharply, almost throwing her against the dashboard, that she came to the present. They were at the bridge but it seemed that there was no bridge there at all. The river had overflowed and the brown, muddy water seemed to be sweeping towards them rapidly.

Jason reversed fast and turned the car.

'Sorry, Tamara,' he muttered. 'Tonight we stay at the hotel. Let's hope they're not full.'

She didn't have any misgiving because she somehow knew it was not going to happen. The river had only just burst over the banks but it was moving fast, and it wasn't the only river. Before they could get back to the hotel they might very well be trapped between two new waterways.

'I don't think we can do it,' she said quietly. 'I know this area. It's downhill all the way to the hotel in the town, and there's another river about three miles back that might well decide to join forces with this one.'

'Are you frightened?' he asked, glancing at her keenly, but she shook her head and met his eyes fearlessly.

'No. Simply pessimistic. I don't expect us to drown, in spite of my earlier, unseemly joke. What I expect is to be waterlogged. This beautiful machine may well have to be left to its fate and we may have to wade a little. The trouble is, I'm not at all sure where we can wade to. It's a bit barren out here, not many signs of habitation until you get to the town.'

'We'll try for the town anyhow,' he said grimly, putting his foot down and giving the car its head. All to no avail. They could see the flood water as they topped the last rise. It must have happened soon after they had passed on their way back.

'Damnation!' Jason snapped. 'This is incredible.'

'Not really,' Tamara stated. 'It's wild up here and we've had unprecedented rain. This is the lowest part and even I know that water has a habit of seeking its lowest course. Take to the hills,' she ordered.

CHAPTER SEVEN

THERE was a small road to the side, and, there being no alternative, Jason obeyed Tamara at once, turning the car and starting along the narrow road.

'I always keep to the main road when I'm coming home,' Tamara informed him, looking out into the gathering gloom. 'I've never been up here, but it seems to me that we have no alternative. The trouble is, I'm not sure if there's any sort of village near here. If there is we can stop and get directions and maybe go home by some circuitous route.'

'We may then find ourselves in further trouble,' Jason muttered, watching the narrow road carefully. 'If there's any sort of accommodation, we take it.'

She wasn't inclined to argue. The whole night seemed fraught with danger and, in any case, she had no wish to spend the night in a wet and bedraggled state in some old barn or other, waiting for it to float away.

Good job Mrs Prost couldn't see them now. She gave a little grin, and Jason must have been attuned to her mood because he glanced at her quickly.

'You like being trapped by floods?' he enquired wryly.

'No. I was thinking of Mrs Prost. She could make a lot out of this, you know. I came against my will and I'm being kept out all night.'

'I don't expect you'll tell her,' Jason surmised drily, and Tamara was suddenly downcast.

'No. It's going to be bad enough if that snoopy photographer realises I never came back in, or if my mother rings and I'm not there.'

'Or if Roger Hart calls and finds you gone?' he asked grimly.

'That too!' Tamara said defiantly. There was no need at all for Jason to know she was all star-struck about him, and it wasn't romantic either, being trapped by flood water, miles from anywhere with no make-up and no nightie and not one bit of comfort. It was different for a man. Men didn't need things about them.

Incredibly, right at the back of beyond there was a village, just a few houses in a little hollow, but there was an inn, a tiny one.

'They won't have accommodation,' Tamara stated gloomily when Jason expressed his satisfaction at this turn of events.

'We'll see,' he stated infuriatingly.

'You could always walk in and buy the place,' Tamara snapped.

'The spoiled-brat syndrome is back, I see,' he murmured scathingly. 'For a while there I thought you had suddenly grown up, no fuss about the floods, no worry about danger; now, with rescue in sight, you're back to normal.'

'I am nothing of the sort,' Tamara said angrily. 'It's pretty obvious that a place so small doesn't cater for travellers.'

He just pulled off road into the parking space at the front and stopped the car.

'Wait here,' he ordered severely and she wouldn't have dared do anything else. She couldn't understand why she argued with him all the time. She didn't want to. It was just that mostly he annoyed her, and she couldn't understand that either. It looked as if she would have to walk on water to get into the place anyhow, she thought glumly. The parking space was waterlogged and Jason must have got his feet wet.

He was back soon and he opened the door for her.

'They have two rooms. Here we are and here we stay. Out!'

'I haven't any things with me,' Tamara complained.

'You'll have to manage. You look perfectly fine without make-up.'

'It's not putting it on, it's getting it off!' she argued.

'This is a small place but clean,' he assured her. 'I imagine that soap will be provided.'

Men knew nothing, Tamara decided. She never mentioned the lack of a nightie. She could do without further caustic comments. She stepped out of the car and water came over her feet, filling her shoes and wetting her trousers.

'This is too much!' she shouted, glaring at Jason in the dim light. 'I'm sure you did this deliberately.'

'As a matter of fact, having got wet myself, I had intended to carry you, but sometimes I get quite tired of your irritating ways. You'd better follow me closely,' he advised sardonically, 'there may be deep holes here and I'm not sure if I would bother to fish you out if you went in up to your neck.' She squelched behind him, filled with hatred. The trousers would clean but the shoes were ruined, and he had done it to put her in her place.

The small inn was cosy, a bright fire burning in the room to the side of the bar. The local custom consisted of two people who ignored them completely, and the landlady assured them that they could have a meal, providing they wanted ham and eggs.

'I'll show you to your rooms,' she offered, 'and then you can come down and have a drink.'

Jason went along to his room, still grimly silent, and the plump middle-aged landlady stayed chatting to Tamara.

'I hear you're stranded. Not for long, though. By morning you'll get clear because when that river floods the road it doesn't stay. Too many fields to fill, you see. We've been expecting it for days.'

'Well, it's nice enough here. Quite an adventure,' Tamara assured her, lying prettily. In fact, it was dismal, the room lit by one naked lamp bulb overhead and a small low-powered lamp at the bedside. 'We haven't anything with us, though,' she continued. 'I even got my feet wet.'

'Your things will dry by morning. I can let you have some night things.' Tamara protested but it was quite useless. A good Samaritan was difficult to keep down. At least she didn't have to wear anything that appeared.

Jason was in the bar when she went down, and they sat by the fire later with their drinks. He seemed to be in a mood, and even when their meal was served he remained silent, only replying monosyllabically when Tamara ventured a remark. It annoyed her and she decided not to tell him about the pyjamas that were about to be forced into his hands. If the size and shape of the landlord was anything to go by they would be very wide and very short. This evil thought amused her no end.

Later she was obliged to clean her face with soap, a highly perfumed variety, and she stood afterwards in her room and contemplated the nightie that had appeared on her bed. It was thick white cotton, two sizes too big but scrupulously clean, and she put it on without too

much resistance. She could hardly sleep in her clothes
and, in any case, her trousers had to dry.

Trouble came when she went back to the bathroom
to clean her teeth. Her finger being the only possible
way to do it, she rubbed vigorously and prepared to sneak
back to her room. Jason was probably asleep already in
the room next door and she was terribly aware that he
was close by. She would have liked to sit up talking to
him but he had been extremely reluctant to have anything to do with her, and, in any case, being with him
was dangerous enough.

When she opened the bathroom door the passage was
in total darkness, and as she peered out the bathroom
light went off too. Tamara fumed silently but it would
be easy to grope her way to her room in this tiny place.
She started very carefully, feeling her way along the wall.

Disaster struck when she met an unexpected obstacle.
An old-fashioned chest along the passage presented a
problem she had overlooked, and her bare foot banged
into it with some force. She gave a subdued and angry
yelp, leaning against the wall and clutching her toe, which
had taken the full force of the blow. It was enough to
bring tears of pain to her eyes and muttering angrily was
sheer necessity.

The door beside her was wrenched open and Jason
was suddenly towering there, his shirt unbuttoned to the
waist and his face aggressively suspicious.

'What the hell are you doing?' His suspicion eased
when he saw her, and he looked simply astonished as
she stood there on one foot, her other foot clutched in
her hand.

'I bumped into this thing. The lights went off.' It was
incredible how a cold foot could hurt after an encounter
with solid wood. She stood upright, gingerly putting her

injuries to the ground, and the action brought her directly in line with the lamp that still shone by Jason's bed.

'My overhead light went off too,' he said vaguely, looking at her with an odd expression on his face. 'It must be some money-saving device.' He moved slowly forward. 'What on earth are you wearing?'

'Oh!' Tamara looked down at her voluminous nightie, having suddenly been made aware of it. 'The landlady lent me this. It's clean. Didn't you get any pyjamas delivered?'

'Blue striped, a curious size,' he murmured, his eyes intently on her. 'I don't need any. Old habits, as you said, die hard.'

'I—er—I'll go, then,' Tamara stammered, her face glowing at this admission that he slept naked. She couldn't stop looking at the muscular power of his chest. She had a ridiculous urge to move against him and rest her face there, feel the crisp dark hair against her cheek. 'Can you leave your door open until...?'

'I'll see you home,' he growled, coming and walking past her to open her door. She had not left her bedside lamp on and he went in to light it. 'All safe and sound,' he added as she hovered at the door. 'You can go to bed with no worries.'

He sounded a bit disgruntled and Tamara came slowly in, her teeth biting at her lip. Perhaps he knew. Perhaps he had caught some of her expression. He wouldn't like to think she was interested. He had thought that before and she had put him straight quite viciously. She wasn't sure if she could do it convincingly now, though.

She just limped past him with a muttered word of thanks, and his hand shot out and caught her arm.

'Let me look at that foot.'

Before she could protest he had her sitting on the bed,
her foot in his hand, his long fingers gently probing.

'Your feet are like ice. I must have been out of my
mind to let you step into the water.'

'It's all right. I'll soon get warm.' She was almost
whispering, and he looked up at her and then stood
quickly, a tight expression on his face.

'Get into bed. I'll close your door on my way out.'
His voice sounded harsh and she stood, turning away to
the bed, her hair hiding her suddenly miserable look.
She was as much a nuisance to him as ever. Every time
they met she had to do something stupid, something to
assure him of her lack of maturity. Everybody else was
very mature at twenty-four. She had been before she'd
met Jason.

'Tamara?' He spoke her name quietly, huskily, but
she didn't turn. 'You look like a child in that astonishing
garment. Something out of the past.' She refused to look
at him even when he turned her and gently tilted her
face. 'Oh, Tamara,' he said softly. 'Tamara.'

His hand cupped her nape, drawing her forward,
pulling her to the hard warmth of his chest, and she got
her wish after all because her cheek rested against the
crisp curling hair that covered the powerful muscles. She
didn't try to move, didn't try to pretend she wanted to
be free, and as he lifted her face she closed her eyes.

'A mixture of fight and submission,' he murmured,
his voice suddenly strained. 'Most of the time I could
shake the life out of you, and then you look at me with
those golden eyes and I want to carry you off with me.'

She opened her eyes then and his face was close, a
taut look on it that made her feel weak. A pulse beat at
the side of his mouth and when he stared into her eyes

she just looked right back until he jerked her forward
and covered her lips with his.

It was no gentle kiss. There was the urgent force of
necessity, masculine need, demandingly possessive, and
the urgency grew as she turned completely into his arms
and linked her own slim arms around his neck. His lips
parted hers and the kiss deepened to passion as her mouth
opened to meet his, and his hands gripped her tightly,
probing her bones through the thick cotton.

'This is crazy,' he murmured unevenly, his lips trailing
across her hot cheeks. 'You know I want you, don't you?'
She could only shake her head. He had said that before
but he couldn't mean it. 'You do!' he said fiercely. 'Every
time I see you I want to take you to bed right at that
moment. I could lock you up and keep you, never let
you go. It's only when you're out of my sight that sanity
returns.'

What was he saying—that she was a temptation but
unsuitable even as a mistress? Did he think she would
willingly...? She gave a little cry and he lifted her right
into his arms, looking down at her bewildered face.

'Yes, it's shocking, isn't it? If you come to me you'll
be burned like a beautiful moth round a flame. I know
it but I still reach for you. Would you come to me,
Tamara? Stay with me?' he asked huskily.

She didn't understand his husky words but she would
take risks for him. She had never risked her emotions
in her life. Emotions were kept for family, for safe things,
but she would risk everything for Jason. She knew it
right then, and his lips covered hers as he saw the answer
in her eyes.

He lowered her to the bed and came down with her,
turning her into his arms, his hands running over her
possessively. 'You're beautiful,' he breathed. 'More al-

luring in this than in that swimsuit even, and God knows I wanted to eat you up then. Now you're not provoking any more. You're demure and trembling, just as you were that night at your flat. I've asked myself a thousand times why I didn't stay.'

His lips were trailing over her cheeks, over her throat, his fingers exploring the shell of her ear, and she shivered with a delight she had never felt before at this gentleness. His fingers unfastened the tiny buttons at the front of the nightie, his mouth moving lower as each small part of silken skin was revealed, and Tamara moaned with pleasure as his hands cupped her breasts, tight and aroused through the thick white cotton.

'Jason!' She twisted wildly and his hand slid inside, his breathing uneven, and she curled against him, sheer instinct telling her what to do.

'It's all right,' he murmured thickly, his voice almost unrecognisable. 'Nothing is going to hurt you.'

His head bent to take the pulsing tip into his mouth, his tongue flicking teasingly against the sharply aware centre, and Tamara cried out, shafts of pain and pleasure surging through her. She arched, trying to escape this ecstasy, but his mouth held her fast, tugging erotically until she reached out blindly and cradled his dark head against her.

'Warm and submissive,' he said huskily, his face between her breasts as he stroked her body with slow heavy hands. 'That's how I like you, all that fiery temper turned to desire, and all for me.'

He moved over her fiercely, his lips crushing hers, and Tamara suddenly remembered the door, the open door, with light in this room and blackness in the passage. If anyone walked past...

'The—the door...' she whispered, clutching him, and for a second he raised his head, his gaze almost dazed before it penetrated his mind that they were lying on her bed for anyone to see. He rolled clear and stood, his shoulders tight and controlled in seconds.

'So much for heated moments,' he murmured ironically. 'Congratulations on keeping your head. Once again, I lost mine.' He turned and pulled the sheets aside, covering her as she lay and looked up at him with hurt, bewildered eyes. 'You would have been more hurt tomorrow,' he stated harshly. 'Tomorrow the world begins again, real live things and real live people. You won't want to remember this.'

'I will,' she said tremulously, a catch in her voice, and his lips twisted in a smile that was all derision.

'Romance lingers in the air. Only it wasn't romance, Tamara, it was desire, wanting, a purely physical need. That's what you should remember.'

He strode out of the room, closing the door, and after a while Tamara put out the lamp and lay in the darkness. For the first time in her life she had been willing simply to give herself to a man. Why? Her mind started to tell her but she twisted away from it. She would never again start something she couldn't finish. She didn't want to know why she was so willing with Jason.

It was just how he was, that irresistible force, a flame to burn her. He knew it; why didn't she? She turned on her side and tried to ignore the wild clamour inside her own body. Why not? Why shouldn't she feel frustrated? She was, after all, as human as anyone else. It was desire, as he had said. She should be grateful to him for stopping. All the same, tears were on her cheeks as she fell asleep.

Jason was extremely silent next morning. Tamara was awakened early with a cup of tea and a smiling suggestion from the landlady that they would want to be on their way. It was pretty obvious that the inn did not need this sort of custom and Tamara dressed rapidly. Her clothes were dry, but her shoes were still very damp and she left them off, padding down the stairs to drink hot tea and eat toast at the side of a silent frowning Jason.

He was no better on the road and Tamara couldn't make idle conversation. Last night was still too much in her mind. As soon as she had seen him her heart had flipped over and his face had reprimanded her as if he knew quite well how she felt. He hadn't forgotten it either, but that didn't help at all. It was a very silent and gloomy trip and she was heartily glad to find that the bridge was now passable. She could not have faced another night like that, even if they had been comfortable, and she had the decided feeling that they wouldn't be made welcome if they went back and asked for further shelter.

Her feelings were very mixed as the town came in sight. Somehow she knew she would not see him again after this. Everything about him told her that and she wanted to cry very badly.

'Would you mind if I didn't take you to your flat?' he suddenly asked in a strained voice. 'I've got a hell of a headache and I can hardly see. I'm not sure if I'm safe to tackle the town traffic.'

One look at his white face told her he wasn't making this up, and she felt a twinge of anxiety.

'I'll get a taxi. Drop me off anywhere. Is it a migraine?'

'No,' he muttered impatiently. 'I don't have anything like that. I expect it's something I've picked up. You'll probably get it too; sorry.'

'I'm very healthy. I've always been healthy. Normally I don't catch things. My dad says it's because I've got a strong immune system and——'

'For God's sake, Tamara, stop lecturing me on your immaculate habits of dental hygiene and your healthy upbringing,' he growled. 'And you'll not get a taxi. You'll take this car. Just drive off when I stumble into my own place.'

'I can't take this! It's a Jaguar!'

'But not the variety that bites. It's a metal box with four wheels, like any other car. Go easy on the accelerator and you'll be fine.'

'If I damage it——'

'I'll buy another. Now shut up before my head rolls off.' He seemed to be having trouble keeping his eyes open, and Tamara kept quiet until he turned down a leafy avenue and drew up in front of a large Victorian house. It had a huge garden and thick hedges, and she felt a twinge of fright as she realised they had arrived and the car would soon be hers to control.

'Slide over and drive off,' he ordered, opening the door. 'I'll have it collected later, maybe tomorrow.'

'Will you be all right?' She slid across and looked up at him anxiously and his lips twisted coldly as he looked down at her.

'Why? You want to come and tuck me up? I thought you were bright as well as beautiful. Intelligence is the ability to learn.'

'I've learned,' she said angrily, her face flushing. 'Christian charity is caring for anyone who is ill.'

'One germ will not turn me into an invalid,' he mocked, even though his face was pale and tired-looking. He was holding in the pain and she could see he needed help, but he had now made it impossible to offer any.

'Then let's hope you make it to the front door,' she snapped. 'If the car isn't collected in a week I'll know the worst. I'll let the company know. I expect Miss Phillips will cope.'

'Sweet charity.' He looked down at her, his lips quirking, and then he turned wearily to the house. 'Mind the damned road,' he added vaguely.

'And see if I'll offer to help again,' she muttered to herself, driving off more smoothly than she had anticipated. How could she care about a man like that? Even when he was ill, in pain, he was domineering, chauvinistic and cruel. She concentrated on the road and before she met any heavy traffic she was well in control of the car. One day, when she was rich, she would buy a car like this. Meanwhile, until it was collected it could sit outside her flat and drive that snooping photographer mad with suspicion.

She changed, had a shower and made herself a meal, but even while she was eating it she was wondering what Jason had had to eat, how he was feeling. There was nobody at all in this town to take care of him. That woman was back in Paris, he had said. She felt miserable at the thought of any woman and it silenced her worries for a while, but as the afternoon wore on she realised that she was thinking about him all the time, worrying herself ragged, and at last she put on jeans and a sweater, collected her coat and bag and went out to the car.

It was really asking for trouble but she wouldn't be able to sleep unless she knew he was all right. If he got annoyed she would tell him she had decided to bring his car back rather than have rumours starting. It seemed like a good excuse, and as dusk began to fall she was once again behind the wheel of a powerful car and heading for the very expensive area where Jason had his house.

There was no sign of life, no lights on, and Tamara's nerve almost deserted her as she drove slowly past the house. At the end of the avenue she turned and came back. It was no use. She had to see if he was all right.

She didn't quite trust her skill to get the car in through the gates and up to the house. It would have to stay right where it was by the edge of the pavement. It left her walking up the drive and she had wild visions of Jason standing in the darkened house and watching her angrily. Knocking on the door took some courage. There was no bell, just a brass knocker, and even after several quite loud knocks no sound came from the darkened house. Jason did not appear.

Nothing would have moved her then. For all she knew, he was collapsed somewhere in there. She searched the key-ring, hoping to find a key to the door, and after two attempts she was successful.

'Jason?' As she stepped into the darkened hall she listened and then called, but there was no answer and she began to search the house determinedly. He might have recovered and gone out, but instinct told her he hadn't.

It was a big house, old, and there were plenty of rooms to search, but she skimmed through them downstairs, not really noticing anything at all, just looking for him. He was upstairs, in the first bedroom she came to, and the sight of him stopped her wild rush. He was in bed in the darkened room, deeply asleep. The sheets had slipped down to expose his bare chest and it suddenly dawned on her that it was freezing in here—the whole house was cold, in fact.

Her own audacity in coming here uninvited made her stand there anxiously for a second, her eyes on him. Even when he was ill, his dark hair damp against his face, he was a disturbing man. There was a sheen of perspiration across his forehead, strands of dark hair falling across it. He moved slightly, stirring in his sleep, groaning, and Tamara was galvanised into action—even a fool could see that he was too ill to be left alone in this bitterly cold place. She might be all manner of a fool for coming here but she was glad she had come all the same.

'Jason?' She moved to the bed and spoke his name softly, intent on finding out just how bad he was, what he needed. 'Jason?' She had to raise her voice and even then it only partly penetrated his mind. His eyes opened a fraction and then closed again as if the effort was too much.

'Jason!' A wave of near-panic hit her; his eyes had been dazed, the pupils enlarged, and her first instinctive thought was to rush out for a doctor. He had only complained of a headache but there was a nasty pallor beneath his tanned skin and clearly he couldn't wake up. '*Jason*!'

The final sharp calling of his name made him stir and come partly to life, his eyes opening fully, but even then he was still dazed, not quite in the world of the living, and he looked at her in a puzzled manner before his lips curved in a satisfied smile.

'Hmm, Tammy.' His hand reached out, his fingers curling round her arm. 'I must be dead—that would explain it.'

'Jason! What have you been taking?' She grabbed his hand, releasing her arm but hanging on to his fingers grimly, scared he would just drift off again. His eyes were closing and she gave his hand a determined shake.

It had the desired effect, her constant use of his name since she had come in finally waking him completely. His eyes snapped open wide, and pain slashed across his face at the effort.

'Hell!' He snatched his hand away and gripped his head, wincing with pain for a second before he turned to glare at her. 'What the devil are you doing here?' He wasn't exactly up to thundering but obviously the thought was there, and Tamara was back to feeling like an intruder. She stood her ground, though, and looked back fearlessly.

'What have you been taking? You look drugged.'

'Pain-killers!' He looked at her furiously. 'Spare me the motherly lecture and get your excuses ready. What the devil are you doing here, sneaking into the house, into my bedroom?'

'I came to bring the car back and there was no light on. I assumed you were collapsed somewhere.' Left with no alternative, she defied him, and his sceptical looks told her he knew perfectly well she was merely on the defensive.

'I told you the car would be collected,' he rasped, 'but, even if I hadn't, does bringing the car give you the right to come inside the house and up here? What did you do with the car? Found it necessary to park it in the kitchen, did you?'

'I'll ignore the fact that you're a hateful and beastly human being,' Tamara snapped, her face red at this cruel goading. 'Normal people worry about each other, but then, you couldn't be expected to know that.'

'Back to sweet charity, are we?' he growled. He slid down in the bed, closing his eyes. 'Get out of here, Tamara.'

It reminded her that, half asleep, he had called her Tammy. Nobody ever did that and she liked the sound of it. It was soft, tender, it made her feel warm and it gave her the nerve to proceed.

'I'm not leaving you in this state, tiresome though you are. You need a doctor.'

'I need peace and quiet and no sign of you,' he grated, his eyes firmly closed. 'I don't have a doctor, I've not been here long enough to find one and in any case I've never needed one in my life.'

'Did you have any alcohol with those pain-killers?' she demanded suspiciously, and his eyes came open again to glare at her.

'I did not, and before you can enquire I'll tell you I took the prescribed dose. Now get out of here!'

'It's freezing in the whole house,' she informed him indignantly.

'And I suppose you've pried your way through each room? This place hasn't been done up yet. Things are old and a bit neglected. The pilot-light had gone out on the boiler when I got back and my head was too bad to bother about heat.' He scowled at her ferociously. 'Why I'm telling you this, I do not know. This head is probably the first sign that I'm sinking to your level of understanding. Go away!'

He slid further down and pulled the sheets up to his ears, and Tamara stared at him in frustration.

'You need something to eat,' she began firmly, but this time he roared at her.

'Out, Tamara! If you're there two seconds from now I'll get up and put you out myself.' In view of the fact that he was wearing exactly nothing, the threat had the desired effect and she went quickly, closing the bedroom door and walking thoughtfully down the stairs. He needed help but he was just too pig-headed to accept it. He needed a doctor, a hot drink, something to eat, and the boiler wanted lighting.

She gave him a few minutes to sink back into that funny sleep and then she started. The doctor was her first call and he took a bit of persuading.

'I'm your doctor, Tamara, not Tysak's,' he protested.

'He hasn't got a doctor,' she pleaded. 'He looks really ill. I'm quite worried. He seems dazed and it needs someone with authority to make him answer questions. He threw me out—verbally,' she added quickly, in case he decided to come.

It lightened the conversation. Dr Harrison knew her father—they had been at medical school together and kept in touch; that was why she had chosen him when she came here.

'Threw you out verbally? Well, that must have taken some doing. I can never manage it. What were you doing there anyhow?'

'It's a long story,' Tamara said uneasily. 'Er—after a business meeting I—er—needed to...'

'Never mind. It sounds as though it will take some time to concoct an excuse. I'll be on my way in a few minutes. And mark this down as a favour to you, my girl. This is Sunday and I only attend the really sick on Sundays.'

'He really is ill,' she assured him, and once again she got that remark that all men seemed to make.

'We'll see.'

She stifled her annoyance and turned her mind to the boiler. She wanted that in action as soon as possible be-

cause, apart from the fact that Jason shouldn't be allowed to get cold, she was freezing herself.

It proved to be a tricky affair. It was in the cellar and
it was a bit spooky down there. Also the boiler looked
like a dangerous old relic, but she found the pilot-light
and after a few minutes and about twelve matches she
had the satisfaction of seeing it burn steadily. She almost
ran for her life when the boiler fired but it seemed to
know what it was doing and, with the cellar steps nego-
tiated and the old door bolted firmly, she turned her
mind to other things.

CHAPTER EIGHT

WHEN Dr Harrison came Tamara pointed him in the right direction and then stayed out of the firing line. She even shut herself in the kitchen just to make sure she didn't hear any raised voices. When it was over she would probably get attacked from two directions, because Dr Harrison wouldn't take kindly to any of Jason's caustic comments.

When she heard him coming down the stairs she went to meet him and drew him into the kitchen.

'How is he?' Her eyes were wide with concern and the doctor eyed her wryly, shaking his head.

'He'll live. I should know better, shouldn't I?' he enquired in amusement. 'I've known you since you were a little girl and you've not altered much. This time, however, you can't control the situation. Tysak is a man with a mind of his own and any attempt to order him about may well be your last stand against tyranny.'

'I only acted because he was ill, and when a friend is ill——'

'What friend are we talking about? I live in this town, you little wretch. I know all about the battle between you and Tysak with those daunting ladies who back you like a flotilla of ships firing broadside.'

'It's not like that now,' she said hurriedly. 'We've got a business arrangement. Yesterday we had a business trip and that's how I knew he was ill.'

'Quite!' He looked at her suspiciously. 'Anyway, he's got a bug. It's going round and he did everything right.

137

No need for me. He took pain-killers and went to bed. It will burn itself out. It's damned cold in here!' he added, glancing round.

'It's all right. I've lit the boiler. Now what shall I give him to eat?'

'Hot soup if he can take it. Plenty to drink.' He looked down at her sternly. 'You can't stay here, Tamara, with a man, especially a man like that.'

'He's perfectly civilised!' Tamara protested, lying vigorously. He was anything but civilised; when Dr Harrison was gone Jason would get up and rage at her. 'In any case, can he manage alone?'

'I expect he could do with a bit of help for a couple of days, but not from you. Hasn't he got hordes of underlings?'

'I imagine he has, in London,' she mused. 'Not here, though.'

'He must have a woman somewhere, a man like that.'

'In Paris.' Tamara bit her lip and tried not to let it bother her. It did bother her, though, and Dr Harrison tipped her face up, watching her intently.

'You shouldn't be here, Tamara,' he insisted. 'Your father wouldn't like it.'

'I'm only going to make him some soup and then I'm going back to my flat. I've got work to do tomorrow. We've got two busy days after the show, and then it's Easter. I'll be going home.'

'Good. You should stay clear of Jason Tysak. You're a babe in arms at the side of somebody like that. Give my regards to Jeffrey and Susan.' He smiled, danger drifting from his mind, and she got him out of the house quite easily.

So far she had managed in spite of opposition. Now for the soup. It would be the most difficult thing because she would have to confront Jason and he would be seething. She was surprised that he hadn't already staggered down to rage at her and throw her out.

He was lying down, but his eyes were wide open when she knocked timidly and went into the room. He hadn't answered and walking in had taken a lot of courage. She tried to look composed but it took an effort because she was anything but composed. She copied the look her mother always had when she was dealing with the ungrateful sick, that usually being her father. It was businesslike, slightly cool, the last shreds of hospital training where her mother had once been a nurse.

'I've brought you some soup,' Tamara informed him briskly, avoiding the dark eyes that followed her progress across the room. 'Dr Harrison's orders.'

'Stop lying, Tamara,' he growled. 'I'm not delirious. Your Dr Harrison made it quite clear that he disapproved of your being here with me. He told me rather threateningly that he was a friend of your father.'

'So he is,' she agreed lightly, putting the tray on the table beside the bed. 'I'm sure he didn't disapprove, in any case. He said quite distinctly that you needed a little help. Anyway, I'm not here for more than a few moments longer. I got the boiler going. I called the doctor, heated a tin of soup and that lets me out.'

'You fiddled about with that dangerous contraption in the cellar?' He pulled himself up in bed to glare at her, but she ignored him.

'It's very cold in here. Pretty soon it will be warmed up. I'll come back when you've had this and I'll leave you a drink before I go.'

Still under the influence of her mother's training, she reached across to fluff up the pillows behind him and he grabbed her arm, looking up at her with dark, angry eyes.

'Stop being charitable! I don't need it.'

'You mean you don't deserve it?' She wrenched her arm free and did some glaring of her own. 'I've helped all I'm about to. You can cope with your headache all by yourself from now on!'

'I warned you about getting burned,' he rasped, his dark eyes staring into hers. 'The ache isn't just in my head. What makes you think I won't drag you into bed with me?'

Tamara fled and she was not amused when she heard that low dark laughter again. He was so hateful! All the same, she stayed to collect his tray and when she went back in with a stiff, angry face he was lying down, already back into that half-drugged sleep. He looked ill. She put the drink by his bed and turned to creep out of the room.

'Thanks, Tamara,' he muttered sleepily. 'The soup was welcome and I'm warm now. I appreciate your help; now go away, there's a good girl. I'll live.'

She cleared up and then got as far as the front door before she turned and looked back up the stairs. She couldn't leave him. Suppose he got worse? Suppose in the night something went wrong? Maybe it wasn't just a bug?

It was quite dark outside now. Nobody would know if she stayed—even Jason wouldn't know. It gave her a feeling of guilty excitement to think of being here with him all night. More than that, it seemed in some odd and unlikely way to give her status in his life, not that he would know it and he had better not find out. Fury would be a very inadequate word if he did.

She carefully slid the bolt on the door and went back into the kitchen. She was hungry. In any case, she couldn't bring herself to give up the pleasure of being near him. She wanted to look after him. It made her happy. Maybe she should have been a nurse? She knew it wasn't that, though. It was Jason. She simply wanted to be close to him.

She smiled ruefully at the thought. She had had a glamorous career already and not once had she felt any twinge of feeling for the handsome men who moved at the edge of that world. Now, out of the smoke of their battle, she saw Jason as necessary to her life.

It was, of course, sheer folly. He was quite right. She would be burned. She might be prepared to fight over lots of things but she knew herself. Inside she was gentle, vulnerable and utterly innocent. Her loving upbringing had allowed her to be like that and it had shielded her through all danger, a barrier to protect her. Now, when she wanted to cast the protection aside, Jason made sure she stayed well away. It was ironic, to say the least.

She ate and then washed up, and when she was sure he was fast asleep she stole up the stairs and found a cupboard with spare bedding. She made a bed up on the settee in the big room at the front of the house. He would turn this into a quite splendid drawing-room, she mused as she tucked herself up for the night. Pity he had chosen this house. She didn't much like it. It was a lonely sort of house, no warmth in it.

Maybe Jason didn't want warmth? She yawned sleepily and turned on her side. She had left one lamp burning. It was an ugly thing and she was sure it didn't belong to Jason. Perhaps he had taken the house with the furniture intact? She was sure he had, on consideration. It would look better when he got the men to it. He might ask her advice when he wasn't so cross. She fell asleep, planning the room's décor.

* * *

It was the noise of the letter-box that woke her as the morning paper was pushed through, and she sat up in a panic, glancing at her watch. Eight o'clock! She had meant to sneak out long before this and there was the shop too. Today they would be run off their feet.

She hastily dressed and folded the sheet and blanket, bundling it under her arm with the pillow and setting off up the stairs as quietly as possible. Heavens, she had to get back to her flat, shower and dress, have her breakfast, and only one hour in which to do it. She didn't even know if Jason was all right to leave.

She was moving with silent speed, back past the bathroom, when she almost knocked Jason down. He was in a dark silk dressing-gown that didn't come much past his knees, and at the sight of him she stopped dead, guilt written all over her face.

'You can't take no for an answer, can you?' he enquired coolly. 'Where did you sleep?'

'On the settee. I—I'll just get you some tea and then I'll——'

'Go back to your flat, Tamara,' he ordered grimly. 'I do not need assistance.'

'You—you look terrible.'

'I'm much better. I'll get my own breakfast and go back to bed. Just let it sink in that I do not want you here.' He looked icily annoyed and Tamara turned away to go back down the stairs, her eyes filling with tears. Well, he couldn't have made it plainer, could he? She was the last person he wanted to see. All the other things had been sheer masculine vanity. The sort of things all men said. Didn't Roger talk like that, after all?

Tears trickled to her cheeks and she bit her lips tightly together, struggling madly when he suddenly reached out for her and pulled her towards him.

'Stop fighting me,' he said huskily, holding her close. 'I know I've hurt you. You may call me all manner of a pig but I'm only thinking of you.' He cradled her against him and tilted her face, grimacing at the sight of the tears on her wet cheeks. 'Don't cry, you beautiful creature,' he warned softly. 'It only puts you more at risk because it brings on an urge to comfort you, and that's the least of my problems.'

When she just looked up at him miserably he wiped at her tears with his fingers, his other arm still around her, his eyes looking into hers.

'I just wanted to help,' she protested in a choked voice, and he smiled ruefully.

'I *do* know that. The trouble is, I need help from other quarters, not from you. From you I want distance.' Her face showed the hurt at these words, her lips trembled, and he muttered angrily, pulling her closer. 'All right,' he said thickly. 'You refuse to understand. Do you understand this?'

She was suddenly wrapped against him, trapped in strong arms, moulded to a body that surged against her. His hand ran down her back, propelling her closer, and the thin silk of his robe might not have been there at all. Certainly it did nothing to disguise the demand of his body, the hard evidence of arousal that thrust against her softness.

His lips sought her frustratedly and she forgot all about the shop as her mouth opened willingly beneath his. There was no gentle coaxing, but wonderful lethargy swept through her and a heat that threatened to melt her completely.

Almost roughly he parted her shirt from the band of her jeans, his hands instantly on her warm skin, and she murmured wildly against his mouth as her arms wound around his neck, leaving him free to take her breasts in his palms and mould them fiercely.

'Now do you understand—do you?' he muttered hotly. 'There's no way you can help me except like this. That is what I want from you, Tamara. This is all I want.'

His hands had been busy dealing with buttons and he peeled her blouse from her shoulders, drawing it down her arms, his eyes hotly on her when she protested weakly.

'Let me look at you,' he ordered thickly. 'I want to look at you, touch you.' His hands spanned her waist and he bent to nuzzle against her breasts, fiercely masculine, demanding the soft submission that came almost instantly. It made him more gentle, some of the ferocity dying away, and he cradled her against him, stroking her breast, his lips over hers. 'Now you know what a bastard I am,' he murmured. 'You come here to help me and this is all I can think of. I've been telling you to go and now I want you to stay. Let me love you,' he pleaded deeply. 'I want you.'

Waves of feeling washed over her. She wanted to stay. She wanted to belong wherever he was.

'Jason,' she said weakly and he drew back to see the answer quite plainly in her eyes. Even while she was looking up into his eyes, ready to agree, she saw the flicker of pain, the way his face whitened, and she came rapidly to her senses, drawing free of him.

'A few more minutes on your feet and you'll collapse,' she assured him with a vigour she certainly didn't feel. 'Get back into bed and I'll bring you some tea and something to eat. I have a shop to open. This is quite ridiculous!'

Instead of anger he was amused, and she noted he had to lean against the wall for support.

'Not entirely ridiculous,' he murmured ironically. 'There is something beautiful in evidence, after all.'

His eyes ran over her and she was made very much aware that her blouse was still hanging open, her breasts, high and pointed right in front of his eyes. She turned away in embarrassment, fumbling with the buttons, and he came to stand behind her, his hands capturing her shoulders.

'I can manage my breakfast,' he said quietly. 'You're going to be very late. Take the car back with you. If it really worries you I'll ring during the day to let you know I'm still alive.'

'Will you?' She turned to look up at him and he made no attempt to hold her again. Instead he smiled into her eyes and then looked at her softly parted lips.

'I promise. Now run along.'

Run along, she mused as she went down the path to the car. Did a lover say that? Stop being a fool, her mind ordered. He was not her lover. There was that woman from Paris for a start and probably plenty more scattered around. 'A man like that', Dr Harrison had said, and it was only what she had thought herself. Why was it that women always thought they could change a man? Her mind was leading her into the old trap and she was following willingly.

It was while she was getting the key into the door of the Jaguar that another car slowed down at the other side of the road. She glanced up with little interest, her mind being completely taken up with Jason, and then she froze into near horror at the sight of Mrs Prost eyeing her oddly before she accelerated and drove off.

That had *really* let the cat out of the bag! It was the last person she would have wished to see here. She got into the car and pulled off, aware very soon that the car in front was going with deliberate slowness as Mrs Prost watched through the rear-view mirror and tried to sum it all up. It would not go unquestioned. Women like that thought they had the right to know every last detail. She swung off towards her flat, wondering what she would say if directly challenged.

The devil prompted her to say, 'Oh, I stayed with him all night.' Jason wouldn't like that, though, and it would give an altogether wrong impression that just might embarrass him. It looked as if subterfuge would be necessary.

She raced to change, swallowed a cup of hot tea and drove to the mews, leaving Jason's car parked outside her flat. Perhaps he would have it collected during the day. It would put an end to things, and she was miserably sure he would think of that.

As usual, the rush of trade after the fashion show was enormous, and they were kept at it all morning. It was only as lunchtime came around that Tamara realised how hungry she was. For the first time in her life she had missed breakfast and they didn't have time for a real break either. Janet went out to get some sandwiches for them both, and while she was out Jason phoned.

'I'm alive,' he volunteered when she answered. She could hear mockery in his voice and she wasn't going to let him know how she felt.

'I'm so glad. We're very busy and I expect I'll be late tonight. Could you arrange for your car to be collected, do you think? It's parked outside my flat.'

'Who's going to care for me?' he asked tauntingly. 'Suppose I fall down the stairs?'

'I think you'll survive. In any case, I've done my stint as Florence Nightingale. I'll have to go now,' she added

as the door opened and Janet came back with the lunch.
'Goodbye.'

'Wait!' He caught her as she was just going to put the
phone down, and she had to admit there was a lump in
her throat at his mockery. He didn't mock then. 'Come
back to me, Tamara,' he asked softly. 'I promise I won't
do a thing wrong. I'll be on my best behaviour.'

Her heart began to hammer, but she wasn't going to
step into any holes again.

'I can't see why——'

'I miss you, damn it! It's utterly miserable being here
alone.'

'How self-pitying. Just like a man,' she managed to
jeer. 'Anyway, I don't like the house.'

'I'll sell it. Come and make dinner for me. I gave you
a pizza,' he reminded her. 'I'll sit demurely and make
polite conversation.'

'I'm not promising.' She knew her cheeks were glowing
and she knew too that she would go but she had to put
up some defence.

'If you don't, I'll get up and come round to your flat,'
he threatened. 'Come early and stay late.'

'Jason!' Her little cry of remonstration was lost on
him.

'I'm missing you,' he said quietly and put the phone
down.

Mrs Prost came in straight after lunch and looked down
her nose somewhat when she saw Tamara.

'Surely I saw you in our part of town this morning?'
she asked sharply.

'Yes.' Tamara decided to face it right then. 'When
somebody is ill I'm afraid it's not in me to ignore it.'

'Jason Tysak? Weren't you driving his car?'

'I was.' Tamara bit back the urge to tell her to mind her own business. 'I'll be taking it back tonight too,' she added for good measure. 'I promised to make him a meal. Dr Harrison thinks he should take care for a couple of days.'

'I'm surprised you were the one to offer your help,' Mrs Prost said bleakly. 'He's caused you a lot of trouble and quite humiliated you.'

'I caused the trouble, Mrs Prost,' Tamara said determinedly. 'The plans that Jason has for the Lancrest Mews are really wonderful. You'll be well pleased. We went to see a place just like it on Saturday. I was most impressed.'

'You went with *him*? The rumours are true, then? I'm quite shocked. At the very least, it's disloyal to us. Staying to take care of him will not do any good for your reputation either.'

'It's called Christian charity, Mrs Prost! Try it!' Tamara snapped, her temper getting the better of diplomacy.

'Is it? And what was it to that other woman who was staying with him? I wonder what kind of charity that was?'

She didn't wait for an answer. She walked out and the way the door slammed shut told Tamara that she had lost a customer. She was quite past caring because all she could hear was the poisonous remark about the other woman. She should have been grateful. After all, it was true, however bitchily said. She needed reminding.

When they finally got the shop closed she went back to her flat, and after great heart-searching she rang Jason.

'I can't come,' she said straight away. 'I'm sorry, but you'll have to manage.'

'It doesn't matter,' he said heavily. 'I'll just sleep. I'm not feeling quite as full of enthusiasm as I was this lunchtime.'

'Are you worse?' Caution left her at the sound of his voice. He seemed to be weary, ill. 'What about your meal?'

'I couldn't eat a thing.' He just put the phone down and Tamara sat there, biting her nails. What was she to do now? It didn't really take much consideration because she already knew she would go to him. She couldn't bear to hear that weariness in his voice and she hated the thought of his needing help and being alone.

'Back to the Jaguar,' she muttered, and this time she took with her the things she would need. If she had to sleep on that settee again at least she would do it in her own nightie.

On the way there she collected things for dinner, parking Jason's car in the High Street with a 'Devil take them all' attitude that lived deep in her character. They were going to talk anyway, so let them. She knew Mrs Prost's prowess as a gossip. What mattered was that she was going to see Jason, and even if he stormed at her she didn't care. The stab of pain when the woman from Paris had been mentioned had told her what she had known for some considerable time. She loved him.

It made her heart sing, even though it was bitter-sweet. He would never love her but when he was gone she would remember this time and clutch it to her for the rest of her days. She drove to his house with a smile on her face and this time she had no qualms about parking where anyone could see. This was her business, hers and Jason's.

When she went up the stairs to his room he was leaning back against the pillows, his eyes on the door as she opened it and just stood there.

'So you came after all?' He looked coldly uncompromising, but she wasn't taking any notice.

'You didn't sound too good on the phone. I changed my mind.'

'I'm never *good*, Tamara,' he taunted. 'Surely you know that?'

'It's none of my business,' she said briskly. 'Live exactly as you want. I'm just the unpaid help.'

She walked out before he could hurt her any more and went straight to the kitchen. It wouldn't take long to make a meal because she had cheated and bought quite a few ready-made things. She got to work straight away because, in spite of her little bag with her nightie and things in the hall, she knew she wasn't staying tonight. There was some modicum of self-protection in her, after all, and she had other things to do besides waiting about for Jason to hurt her with his caustic comments.

When she looked up he was leaning in the doorway, watching her, his eyes heavy and dark. He had dressed in casual clothes, grey trousers and a black sweater, and she just stared at him in astonishment.

'Should you be up?' She was defensive and he could see that.

'Probably not, but all the same I'm here.' He walked across and sat at the kitchen table, his chin resting in his hands as if he had to hold his head up, and Tamara had to stifle the urge to go to him and beg him to go back to bed.

'Can I have a drink?' he asked after a while when she got on vigorously and ignored him.

'Water or tea?' She didn't even turn round, and she heard his quiet laugh.

'No use asking for a whisky, I expect?'

'None whatever. You know perfectly well that with those tablets you shouldn't have alcohol.'

'Tea?' he enquired with such meekness that she shot him a suspicious look before she broke off to make it. She took good care to keep clear of him too and she acted as if he weren't there at all, only answering briefly when he spoke.

They stayed where they were for the meal and as far as Tamara was concerned it was a very difficult time. Every time she looked up Jason's eyes met hers, and, although his looks taunted, she could see perfectly well that he should not be out of bed at all.

It was not until she walked past him to load the things into an ancient dishwasher he had pointed out that she made any mistakes at all. She passed too close and he grabbed her, pulling her down on to his knee and holding her fast.

'Now, then, Miss Trouble,' he said sternly. 'I want some answers. Why did you refuse to come after I begged so humbly? Why did you change your mind? And what's all this silence about?'

'I—I shouldn't be here, sitting here . . .'

'Possibly not, but I'm enjoying it. I'll let you go when I've heard a few confessions.'

It looked as if he meant it, and in any case she was back to mindless excitement, ignoring danger, as usual.

'Mrs Prost saw me leave this morning,' she said stiffly, not about to let him know how she felt at all.

'Ah! The champion gossip. And then what?'

'She came to the shop to pry and ended up remonstrating with me,' Tamara said quietly. 'Luckily there was only Janet there.'

'I imagine you had a good excuse ready?' he enquired wryly, and it annoyed her instantly.

'I did not! Why should I wriggle about, lying to her? I snapped at her and she left haughtily.'

She looked at him angrily and he was grinning at her, laughter back in his eyes.

'So, little wild-cat, you lost a good customer? You realise she'll spread it all around the town?'

'I'll sue her!' Tamara said hotly. 'She'd better be careful what she says!'

'I think she probably will be,' he assured her softly, 'especially if she mentions it to her husband first. You see, I've opened an account at the bank and he happens to be the manager. I'm sorry to say that managers tend to drool a bit over a Tysak account.'

'Why—why have you...?' She had a sudden burst of hope that he really intended to stay here, and he put his hand against her face, looking at her intently.

'I'm not sinking the firm's money into the town, don't worry,' he said drily. 'Just some of my personal account. It's convenient.'

His hand was warm against her face and she knew she should move away but she didn't. His eyes were running over the creamy satin of her skin and she could see desire beginning to flare in the dark depths of his gaze. It would bring them back to the same state of affairs, destroy this momentary warmth.

Tamara jumped up, escaping and moving rapidly away from him. She ignored the flash of emotion that crossed his face. She had emotions too, and Jason had turned her world upside-down.

'Well, good!' She began to tidy up the kitchen, hastily pushing things into cupboards. 'If it keeps her quiet it will have been quite worthwhile.'

'Are you scared to look at me?' he asked softly when she kept her face turned away, no matter where she happened to be at that second.

'I'm not particularly scared of anyone.' It was a bit tricky to keep control of her voice, and she moved to another tack before he could go on. 'Did I tell you that we're closing down early for Easter? At the moment we're extremely busy and normally this sort of pressure comes for about two days after the fashion show. Things get slack then, so this year we're closing early.'

'And then what?' She could tell that he had turned to look right at her and she kept her head down, rubbing the sink vigorously to no good purpose.

'I go home, of course. I won't come back until the Wednesday after Easter.'

'You'll be away for a week.' He sounded weary again, but she kept up her jaunty manner.

'Good reckoning. One whole week of bliss, nothing but country air and home cooking. I expect we'll have a houseful of relatives over Easter. It usually happens. It's a happy time. We decorate the house, you know, like Christmas, but with spring flowers and forsythia and a lot of newly sprung green branches. It's our tradition. My grandmother started it—that's my father's mother, of course. Mum kept it up because it's family. There have been Rawsons in that part of the country for generations.'

'Tamara! Shut up!'

Jason sounded almost violent and she stopped at once,
like a tap turned off. She knew perfectly well she had
been babbling on like a scared schoolgirl, and she wasn't
a bit surprised when he got up and walked out of the
room.

CHAPTER NINE

JASON wasn't anywhere to be seen when Tamara was ready to leave, and it looked as if he had gone back to bed. Well, he should never have been up anyway. She tried not to sink into misery. She kept up a brisk attitude and took him a drink before she left, and she knew perfectly well that she wouldn't come back again. There was nothing between her and Jason, after all. He didn't want any attachment and that was so obvious. After tomorrow she somehow knew she wouldn't see him again. She was going to go away, take an attitude of self-defence, run home to her mother, cry into her pillow and try to put him out of her mind.

He wasn't in bed when she went cautiously to his room. The door was open, the lamps on, and she hesitated and then went in, determined to finish this off with some dignity and courage. Whatever she felt, Jason wouldn't know it.

He was standing by the window, just staring out into the darkness through the partly drawn curtains. He was still dressed, and as she went in he turned and looked at her sombrely.

'Not gone yet?' He sounded bleak, his voice heavy, and she clung on to her brisk image for all she was worth because it was all she had.

'Just going. Here's your drink. I'll put it near the bed.' He made no reply and she moved quickly to the bedside table, her face once again turned away, searching both for something to say and some way of telling him she

would not come again. 'I wish you would get somebody
to collect your car,' she got out a bit desperately. 'I'll
be packing to go tomorrow night and then the flat will
be empty for a whole week. I—I'm not sure if it will be
safe just left there. I—I mean, somebody might scratch
it for—for spite because it's such a beautiful car. People
do things like that and...'

She had no idea he had moved until his hand came
to her shoulder, moving upwards to brush her hair aside
and expose the tender nape, where her bent head made
her so vulnerable. His hands gripped her shoulders
gently, pulling them back to him, and his lips brushed
her neck beneath the red-gold shine of hair that fell
forward in a silken swath.

'There's no need to talk so frantically,' he murmured,
his lips against her skin. 'I know you're scared. You've
hardly stopped trembling since we first met.' He turned
her slowly, looking down at her when she hung her head
and refused to meet his gaze. 'You're sensible, too,
running home to Mother and that great extended family,
that safe family.'

'I'm not running!' She looked up to protest and met
dark eyes that were vibrant with feeling. 'It's Easter. I'm
just going h-home...'

'Take care, then,' he warned softly. 'Avoid floods and
small hotels.'

'I will.' She moved away, filled with bitter pain when
he let her go readily. By the time she came back he would
probably be gone, right out of her life. There was something in his face that told her so and she didn't want to
look at him again in case she cried.

'Tammy!' His voice stopped her when she was no more
than a step away from him, and at the warm sound of
that little change to her name she turned back. It was

almost like loving, caring, the sort of thing you said to a child you adored, and it drew her eyes to his face in a helpless sort of pleading.

His own face was tight, stiff with feeling, his mouth almost harsh. That pulse was beating again by his jaw and there was a raw look in his eyes that held her spellbound. When he spoke his voice was rough, and he looked at her blindly, a terrible look that almost stopped her heart.

'Going home is the most sensible thing you could do,' he said in a stilted voice. 'If you go I'll know it's for the best and I'll go too. The project doesn't need me. It will just go on. You'll be sensible and I'll be wise.' His eyes ran over her face, seeing the unhappiness, the unshed tears, and he reached out for her, jerking her towards him as if he couldn't help himself. 'But I don't want to be wise. Stay with me, Tamara! Stay with me! Oh, God, I need you!'

He buried his face in the warmth of her neck and she clung to him as she had wanted to do so often, so filled with tearful happiness that talking was impossible. There wasn't one doubt in her mind. She belonged to Jason, possibly from the first moment she had seen him. That driving force had attracted her like a bird to the sunlight, a moth to the flame—irresistible, overwhelming.

He tilted her face, taking it in two hands that shook with passion, his words breathed into her mouth.

'I want you and I can't fight it any longer. I want to make love to you, sleep with you in my arms, feel your skin against mine. Stay with me!'

She was trembling too much to answer. Her lips sought his blindly and he crushed her to him, his mouth opening over hers, demanding, devouring, a wild rush of passion that left her weak. Molten feeling ran through her as his hands caressed her urgently and she knew that, whatever happened now, the rest of her life would be filled with the wonder of this moment, because everything about him told her there was no stepping back. She never even thought of it. There was a feeling of belonging that overwhelmed her.

There was passion in Jason that she felt like a storm, his hands impatient as they moved over her, finding the soft surge of her breasts and grasping them through the fine wool of her sweater. His low groan told her it wasn't enough and he pulled the garment over her head, tossing it down with his own and propelling her back into his arms. Moans of pleasure mingled in their warm breath as their skin met for the first time, and Tamara clung to him, lifting her face to his.

Jason's lips devoured her, his hands on her breasts, his thumbs rubbing erotically over the darkened nipples until she sagged against him, every bone melting, only her arms around his neck keeping her upright.

'Come to me, Tammy,' he demanded deeply, his lips trailing like fire over her skin. 'Melt into me, need me!' His teeth fastened on her ear, biting passionately at the tender lobe as his fingers moved with impatience to the zip of her jeans, propelling it down so that they just clung to her hips. It gave him access to her skin and his hands slid inside the waistband, finding the warmth, slowly caressing the rounded length of her thighs.

It was something she had never known, this feeling of being completely taken over, a brilliantly soaring excitement growing inside her that drove all caution away. She moved against him, her actions purely instinctive, rhythmical, until he growled low in his throat and sank his mouth against her neck with hungry pressure, tightening her to him until she was breathless.

Tamara cried out. She wanted to be part of him, her mind utterly bewitched, and her hands sought the smooth skin of his back, moving over it, exploring, her fingers curled and feline, urging him closer until the coiled passion inside him snapped and his mouth came back to crush hers, his tongue forcing itself between her lips in an act of possession that left her trembling even more. She was so given up to feeling that nothing else entered her mind, not the thought of the end of this or the thought that Jason accepted her actions as if she were accustomed to a lover.

The sudden, strong, pulsing movement of his tongue excited her more, made her shake with desire; little incoherent whispers came from her throat as he moved her to strip off her clothes, and she lay exactly where he put her on the bed, her eyes closed, her body tossing in torment as he undressed, his dark eyes burning down at her.

She felt him move close and her hands reached out for him, his name a frenzied whisper in her throat, but he stayed out of her reach, tormenting her, capturing her hands in one of his, running his free hand down her body until she gave a whimpering cry like a lost soul, all the yearning she felt inside encapsulated in that one sound.

'Soon, darling. Very soon,' he promised thickly, relenting enough to release her hands and let them sink into the thick darkness of his hair as he bent to caress every part of her slender shape. Her restless movements brought further heat to him, but when his hand slid between her thighs and his head bent lower to join it she cried out in shocked protest.

'No! Jason, please!'

'Yes! Relax, darling. Enjoy everything.' His persistent caresses brought sobs to her throat. She had not given any thought to this, had not even imagined it. She was overwhelmed at her own innocence, ashamed to be so inexperienced because he would know soon enough and he would reject her. Being with Jason was like a dream, but she wasn't right in this dream. He would find out how little she knew, how far from him she really was. How could she ever have hoped to match his skill?

'Please, Jason! I've never... I don't know what to do.'

He lifted his head and looked up at her, his eyes like flame and his body quite still.

'Tamara?' He sounded stunned and words would not leave her trembling lips. 'You're a virgin?' he asked huskily. 'I'm the first man who ever did this to you, held you like this?'

'I—I'm sorry...'

'Sorry?' His eyes swept over her, lingering on each part of her nakedness. 'God help me, I'm not sorry. I want it to be me. The thought of any other man touching you is enough to drive me insane.'

His hand caressed her stomach heavily, making her breath leave her lips in a trembling sigh that seemed to weaken her whole body and melt her back to submission. She could hardly believe that he was glad, that he wanted to teach her everything, but now there was tenderness that cloaked his fierce desire and her limbs melted, relaxed while heat flooded every part of her as he went back to his persistent caressing.

When he moved to lie covering her, his hands moulding her breasts, she clutched him tightly, her small even teeth biting into his shoulder, her fingers digging into the taut, strong muscles, her body moving to accommodate him as he moved against her demandingly.

'Now ask me to love you,' he whispered against her lips. 'Ask me, Tammy. Beg for it. It's what I want to hear.'

'Please, Jason!' She arched against him wildly, spasms already starting deep inside her, wanting something she could only imagine but wanting it urgently. 'You're cruel!' The accusation seemed to be torn from her and he gathered her close, his face against hers.

'Cruel? To *you*? How could I be?' He moved against her fiercely, his weight a wonderful burden as his lips cut off her wild cry of pain and passion at the strong thrust of his desire. 'Tammy!' He held her fast, his face rubbing against her burning cheeks. 'Relax, darling. I've got you safe. It's all right.'

The burst of pain passed as if it had never been and she gasped as he began to move inside her, her woman's body joining the rhythm, her arms tightening until their lips fused together and release came in a rush of a thousand wings, a swirl of gold and silver stars and black, velvet oblivion.

When she managed to open her eyes he was leaning over her, watching her, his gaze roaming over her face. He said nothing at all and she suddenly realised there were tears on her face, tears he was quite aware of. She lifted her fingers to brush them away unsteadily, but he caught her face between his hands, tilting her head and gathering the tears with his lips.

'I—I didn't expect to cry,' she whispered tremulously, knowing he would be astonished at tears.

'If you hadn't I would have been disappointed,' he murmured huskily, his lips trailing over her cheeks. 'I would have known that the feeling didn't go deep

enough.' He drew back to look at her, his eyes holding
hers. 'You gave me everything, Tammy, not just your
lovely body. You gave me something from deep inside
you. That's never happened to me before.'

She didn't understand; her golden eyes moved over
his face, puzzled, alarmed at his intent, sombre
expression.

'Didn't you like it?' she asked worriedly. He didn't
answer. He just moved to his side and gathered her close
but, even with her head on his shoulder, his arm tightly
around her, she was anxious about it.

'Jason? D-didn't you like it?'

'Like it? I'll never be alive again,' he said softly. 'I've
been thrown out of heaven. Maybe it would have been
better to remain in blissful ignorance. Go to sleep now.
It will be morning all too soon.'

Tamara wanted to stay awake, to know that she was
close to him, wrapped in his arms. After such a shat-
teringly emotional experience she seemed to be only
shakily clinging to reality. It had happened too quickly,
been over almost as soon as it had started, and Jason
was still a stranger, a stranger who owned her body and
soul.

Sleep seemed to creep up on her, stealthily closing her
eyes, and she protested plaintively, murmuring against
his shoulder.

'Sleep.' He curled her against him, turning to face her,
his hand massaging her nape until a smile drifted across
her lips and sleep came like a friend.

Once again she woke up late. Jason was still sleeping
beside her, a deep heavy sleep that worried her for a few
seconds. She hadn't stirred throughout the night, but as
she woke up she was instantly aware of her sur-

roundings, deliriously happy to find Jason there beside her. It was like being singingly alive for the first time.

She wanted to wake him up, talk to him, but there was the shop. As before, she was quite unprepared for the day. There was so much to do, and now she wouldn't go home, not unless Jason went with her. She wanted him to go with her very much, to welcome him into the safety of her family, to let him feel the love, but he would have to decide that.

She dressed quickly and silently, creeping from the room. She would make breakfast for him before she went. She would only wake him then. Maybe she would come back at lunchtime to talk. The time was passing much too quickly because she was still dreamily lethargic, moving at half speed, a smile on her lips. This morning she was a different person. She felt different and she longed to see Jason smile at her, hear him say her name in that deep, drowsy voice.

When somebody knocked on the door she raced to it in case they woke him before she was ready with his breakfast. All manner of things were flying through her head. She was planning the day, planning the holiday, wondering if this was the post and why he had felt it necessary to knock. It must be a parcel, she decided as she opened the door to the cool air of the morning.

It was not the post, and Tamara's world seemed to shatter around her as she saw the woman who stood there. She had come back, back from Paris, this woman who stayed with Jason.

'Hello? You look familiar.' Claire just walked in as if she lived there, and Tamara backed away in face of such assurance. Nobody would be assured with Jason unless he wanted them to be. 'Ah! Now I've got it! You're the girl from the fashion show. The one who infuriated Jason. Have you been making it up with him, then?'

'He's ill. I—I just popped in to see if he wanted anything but I don't think he's up yet.' It was astonishing how speedily the mind worked under pressure, how easily it prepared a defence. 'As you're here, you'll want to take over. You're Claire, aren't you?'

'Claire Devereux.' The woman bit her lip and looked anything but pleased. 'What's wrong with him? He's never been ill in his life.'

'It's a—a bug. It's going round; the doctor said that——'

'Damn! I need him. I was banking on taking him back with me today.'

'Well, I—I'm sorry. I have to go now. I'm late as it is. I only just popped in.'

Tamara retreated, snatching up her things and making for the door. She didn't want to be around when they greeted each other. She didn't want to hear Jason consoling this woman because he wasn't fit to go with her.

'I suppose I'd better go up and see to him,' Claire said unwillingly. 'Thank you. It was good of you to help him, considering his annoyance with you, Miss...?'

'Rawson, Tamara Rawson. I'll have to go. I—I'm late.'

She almost ran out of the door, shutting it behind her and going blindly down the path, her mind not really working. It was only as she found herself halfway down the road that she realised she had left the car behind and that she would be later than ever. She stumbled into a phone booth and called a taxi.

There were few customers during the morning, in spite of the fashion show. Janet was gloomy about it but Tamara hardly noticed. All she could think of was Jason and the night they had spent together. He had wanted her, wanted to sleep with her, and she had been more than willing. How could she blame him?

Pain tore into her when she thought of Claire Devereux at the house, thought of her sitting by Jason, talking to him, making love. What a fool she had been to walk willingly into the force of his desire. He had never mentioned love, never spoken of anything but wanting. Did it matter that he said her name tenderly, called her Tammy when he was sleepy?

Over and over she glanced at her watch, ashamed when she realised she had been waiting for him to ring, waiting for him to beg her to go back. She had wanted him to call and say that Claire meant nothing to him, but he wasn't going to call. By now he would be up if he was well enough. He might even be on his way to Paris. He had been well enough to make love to her the night before—passionately.

Tamara's cheeks burned at the memory and she bit into her lips hard to stop tears coming. If only this day would end. If only she could get away.

'I really think we're being boycotted!' Janet said with annoyance as lunchtime approached and the trickle of custom became even thinner. 'Normally we've been run off our feet for two days after the show, and don't forget either that it's Easter coming up. What with the show and Easter, we should be bursting at the seams, and look—nobody!'

Tamara brought herself to the present with difficulty. It was quite true. This was an unusual turn of events.

'Do you think Mrs Prost...?'

'I certainly do!' Janet muttered angrily. 'That woman got brought down to size, probably for the first time in her life. She's been round her cronies and spread the word, believe me. I know that lot. I've lived in this town all my life.'

'Maybe I should learn to hold my tongue,' Tamara mused, but Janet scoffed that to oblivion.

'Why should you? She's an interfering busybody.'

'And we're almost empty,' Tamara sighed.

'They'll be back!' Janet stated emphatically. 'They need the clothes and they need your advice. I can't count the times you've saved them from walking off in something that was utterly unsuitable. They'll come back, and when they do we have the upper hand and we'll not lose it again. We'll condescend a bit, like all high-class shops.'

It brought a smile to Tamara's face for the first time that day.

'You're a great tonic,' she admitted. 'How would you feel if I went off now? I'm going home tomorrow and I've got a lot to do. I know you were only going to take on the shop by yourself for the last three days, but——'

'Get off now,' Janet urged. 'Nothing seems to be happening here and if it suddenly all happens I can cope. Go on! It's a long way to Cumbria.'

It was only as Tamara prepared to leave that Janet said anything else.

'Are you in love with him, Tamara?'

'Roger? Good heavens, no!' Tamara tried to look amused but it didn't quite come off and Janet regarded her solemnly.

'You know I'm talking about Jason Tysak. I *did* hear what Madam Prost said, after all, and I saw your face. Being keen on somebody is one thing; being prepared to look after them when they're ill is another, especially as you must have known that somebody would see you there.'

'It was simply Christian charity, as I told——'

'All right. I'll mind my own business. What do I do if he rings?'

'He won't ring,' Tamara said quietly, going to the door. 'I'll see you after Easter, Janet, and I'll make this up to you.'

'No need. If you have to run I can cover for you with no trouble.'

Yes, she was running. Tamara admitted it to herself. Jason had simply dismissed their night together or he would have telephoned already, even if he was ill. Claire was there now, though. He didn't need anyone else. She packed hurriedly, feeling she was under tremendous pressure to escape from the town and everyone in it.

She cried all the time as she packed and the beauty of the night before drained away into bitterness and misery. Jason had said he would never be alive again. Words! So many words. She was the one who would never forget. She was doing something she had not had to do all the time she had been in London. She was running for home, for safety and for comfort.

Tamara set off before she had even eaten lunch. She was not going to go on feeling this trapped, hopeless creature she had become. She planned carefully. Going straight home would be unfair. She would simply walk in and blurt out her unhappiness, making everyone else unhappy too. She wouldn't arrive in the dark either. She would stay at some hotel on the way, hide for the rest of the day, if only from herself. Tomorrow she would go home and start again somehow.

She skirted the town, taking a ridiculously long way round, chiding herself for foolishness. What was she expecting, after all? Did she imagine that Jason would be out looking for her? He wasn't looking for her, not even thinking of her, or he would have phoned while she was at the shop. She didn't stop for lunch and by the time she found a hotel it was sheer necessity that stopped her. Her nerves were tight, over-stretched, and all she wanted to do was sleep and forget.

'Shall we try to eat lunch outside?' Susan Rawson popped her head out of the house and smiled at Tamara and the young man who sat beside her and teased relentlessly.

'You're worried about having me back indoors, Aunt Sue?' Robbie Breck turned his teasing blue eyes on his aunt and gave Tamara a moment's respite.

'Of course!' Tamara's mother retorted, well used to his ways. 'You can't cause much damage out of doors. Well, what do you think, Tamara?'

'It's unexpectedly warm,' Tamara agreed, glancing up at the sky. 'We could chance it.'

'Good. It's a bit of a nuisance, Easter being so early. I don't like any traditions upset. We eat lunch out of doors at Easter—always have done.'

'Pneumonia notwithstanding,' Robbie murmured as his aunt went inside. 'Isn't she a wonderful thing, though, Tam? I don't get here nearly so often now, what with the business and everything. It's great that you're back too.'

Tamara smiled across at him. It was good to have Rob here. He had come yesterday, shortly after she had arrived, and it had helped to get her through the evening without any deep discussions with her mother. They all knew each other much too well, she thought ruefully. She hadn't missed the alert look on her mother's face as she had come through the door. Neither had she missed the glances that had been exchanged between her mother and father.

They had left her to settle in, to come round, like the sensible, loving people they were, but soon she would be faced with some sort of mild interrogation. She had to have her story sorted out by then. The fact that Rob had arrived almost on her heels had given her a short reprieve but it would all come out later, as much of it as she wanted to tell.

'How's the business?' she asked, leaning back in the garden chair and slanting a look at her cousin's good-looking, laughter-filled face.

'Good. Very good,' he conceded with satisfaction. 'I'm getting orders from all over the country.'

'How can a firm that makes mock-antiques do so well?' Tamara asked with deliberate scorn.

'*Mock*? Wretched female! These are the antiques of tomorrow. I don't go round copying things. This is original. Bespoke furniture!'

'I know, but it's only sort of crafty woodwork isn't it?' Tamara teased, getting her own back for a whole morning of torment, her usual treatment from her much loved cousin.

'Crafty woodwork?' He sprang up at her and Tamara raced for the safety of the apple tree with Rob in hot pursuit, eager violence on his face.

He caught her arm and swung her round, and her shrieks of laughter were suddenly stilled as her mother came to the door, smiling at these usual antics.

'Do try to be civilised, you two,' she chided laughingly. 'Tamara has a visitor.'

Tamara had not needed to be told. She had already seen the tall dark man who stood beside her mother.

Jason's eyes were on both of them and there was the same black ice there she had seen often before.

'I'm interrupting,' he said politely, his voice unbelievably stiff. 'I should have let you know.'

'You're not interrupting,' Rob informed him cheerfully, slackening his arm-lock on Tamara's neck. 'You've just saved Tam from injury. I'll get her later but I might not be so incensed by then. The punishment might not quite fit the crime.'

'I'll get some tea for you all,' Susan Rawson said cheerfully, her eyes darting from Tamara's suddenly white face to Jason's grim expression. 'It's at least half an hour to lunch. We're waiting for Jeffrey, you see. Of course you'll stay, Mr Tysak?'

She didn't wait for an answer and for a minute Tamara thought Jason wasn't about to move. Rob saw to that.

'Sit here,' he ordered. 'Take the seat between me and Tam. It might save her from attack.'

It was clear that Jason was not finding this amusing and, after one quick look at his face, Rob shot off into the house, muttering that he would help with the tea-tray. It left Tamara facing Jason, and she could think of nothing at all to say. He took matters into his hands.

'I've brought the lease for you to sign,' he said tightly. 'The others have signed theirs.'

'I could have signed it after Easter,' Tamara murmured, filled with embarrassment, and trembling. 'There was no need for you to go to all this trouble.'

'I want everything wrapped up before I go away.' There was no sign of a smile, no sign that he even remembered the other night. Tamara risked a quick glance at him and then looked away again, wondering how she was going to live through the afternoon.

'I see.' She looked down at her hands and Jason drew his breath in through clenched teeth.

'Do you?' he rasped. She was saved from more anger by the arrival of her mother and Rob, both of them looking determinedly cheerful, and Tamara sprang up nervously to help set out the tea-tray.

'J-Jason has come to bring me the lease to sign,' she said brightly, getting a quick glance from her mother as she said his name.

'Well, that's nice. Everything's settled, then.' Her mother beamed determinedly and Jason smiled that tight smile that Tamara knew so well.

'Completely settled,' he stated harshly. He was dangerous again, a savage just below the skin, his dark eyes like menacing pools. It was only her mother's presence that held him in check and Tamara knew it. Instinctively Rob knew it too and his teasing chatter stopped altogether. He glanced at Tamara from the corner of his eye and winked soothingly when he saw her pale face, her anxiety. Unfortunately Jason saw it too and stood with one swift, almost violent movement.

'I'm sorry,' he said politely to her mother. 'I have very little time and I must talk to Tamara. Could we have a few minutes alone, do you think?'

'Of course. I have to get on with lunch in any case, and Rob can help me. He hasn't done his share today at all. Why don't you go for a walk by the wood, darling?' she added, turning slightly worried eyes on Tamara. 'You can talk—er—business there and work up an appetite for lunch.'

Tamara thought the appetite wouldn't be there at all, probably never again, for that matter, but she nodded and smiled weakly, and Jason took her arm in a deceptively calm grip and nodded his thanks. She didn't pull her arm away, because she knew he would explode. He was violence waiting to happen. He had come like a storm to their sunny morning, a marauder, quite outside their understanding. Even she didn't know why he was so angry, unless it was that he was annoyed at having to come all the way here with the lease.

She moved her arm carefully out of his grip when the house was no longer in sight. They were walking on a path parallel to the woods, a fence at the other side of them cut off a field and the hills started behind it. He said nothing until they were almost at the outer edge of the wood, in a clearing where the path widened.

'I'm sorry I interrupted your time with Rob,' he said harshly. 'Obviously I had no idea.'

'No idea of what?' Tamara looked at him in nervous surprise.

'No idea you had someone tucked away up here,' he rasped. 'I can see why you shot off so quickly.' It dawned then, and Tamara's golden eyes opened wide with annoyance.

'Robbie is my cousin!' she snapped. 'My first cousin. One of the family! Even if he weren't, it would surely be none of your business. I didn't enquire about Claire. I even left her to take over, reluctant though she was to worry about your health.'

It seemed to make him more annoyed than ever, with no sign of guilt. He grabbed her arms and almost slammed her to the fence, towering over her fiercely.

'Claire is my sister!' he grated, looking at her as if he dared her to doubt it. She *did* doubt it.

'You said she was a part-time occupation. You implied that——'

'She is a part-time occupation,' he muttered furiously, 'one I could well do without.'

'She's French!' Tamara snapped bitterly. 'How can she be your sister with a French name?'

'It's her husband's name,' Jason said tightly. 'She divorced him, but she can't leave things alone. She wants to go back. I escort her back and within days she's quarrelling again and racing to England and me. When I move I'm keeping my change of address secret. They can sort out their lives without my assistance.'

It left many things unanswered but at that moment Tamara was not looking further than the fact that Claire Devereux was not his girlfriend, not staying with him because he wanted her. She was his sister and he had been jealous of Rob.

'Why did you let me believe . . .?' she asked softly, but his answer silenced her, made the colour fade from her cheeks again.

'Because I wanted to keep you out of my life,' he told her tightly. 'I wanted nothing to do with you at all. You walked into my path, Tamara, and you kept on coming. Nothing would deter you.' He gave a soft, bitter laugh. 'I thought I could handle it but I couldn't. I still can't handle it, so I'm tying up the loose ends and moving on.'

CHAPTER TEN

'I'M A—a loose end?' Tamara asked in a choking voice, fighting with tears at this cruel way of speaking, this cruel way of thinking. She cringed when Jason gave that hard low laugh again.

'Oh, yes,' he said quietly, 'the biggest one there is. That's why I'm going and not coming back at all. Believe me, it's better that way.'

'Better for you!'

'Better for both of us.' He turned away, looking out over the fields, his jaw tight. 'I'm in love with you, Tamara.'

It hit her like an arrow, deep inside, a shaft of beautiful feeling that made her legs weak. In that moment she was glad she was standing against the fence. He loved her! He couldn't mean it about leaving. She must be dreaming.

'I—I don't understand...' she began shakily. He glanced at her white face and then looked away again.

'Neither do I. It's never happened to me before and I never expected it to happen. I could do without it.'

'Don't you want to—to love me?' Tamara whispered. Her hand came to his arm almost timidly and he looked down at her slender fingers. She felt the muscles of his arm tighten as if he wanted her to go away, but she still stood there, looking up at him.

'No. I don't want to love you—anyone but you, Tamara. You need marriage, children, a warm family, and you don't need that from me. I'm almost thirty-seven.'

'What has that got to do with it? I'm nearly twenty-five. Why, over Easter——'

'I will never get married,' Jason interrupted grimly. 'I've seen marriage—my parents, my sister. I know what happens to children when a marriage breaks up. I've experienced it and seen it all too often. Almost everyone I know is either divorced or contemplating it. That's not for me.'

'How can you say that just because you've seen it the same will happen if——?'

'One day you'll meet someone of your own enchanting age,' he said wearily. He turned and saw the tears in her eyes and moved to take her in his arms, but stopped abruptly. 'Oh, Tammy. I wanted you so much. I couldn't resist you in the end and you gave me everything.' He grimaced ruefully. 'Oh, I could live with you. I could live with you for the rest of my life in all probability, but I wouldn't even ask you. You're not like me.' He looked round, across the hills, down at the house nestling beyond the trees. 'All this. This is you. Family, affection, more than all my wealth. One day you would leave me. I just couldn't face it.'

'I wouldn't leave you, Jason,' she said softly and he turned his head back and looked down at her with a wry smile.

'Now perhaps you think not. You'll change, Tamara. You'll change and grow. I will never change. I'm bitter about marriage right through to the bone. One day perhaps I'll have a comfortable arrangement with some woman. Some woman who will simply be a partner. Maybe I'll even love her a little.' He looked deeply into her eyes. 'But not you, Tammy, not you. Loving you might just kill me.'

'I—I'll live with you,' Tamara said desperately, not understanding at all the feelings that were eating him up.

'I'll never ask you,' he said softly. 'I know the sort of life you need. Go out and get it. Forget me.'

'How do you expect me to do that?' She hung her head, her hair curtaining her face, and he came close, tilting her chin. For a while he just looked at her and then his hand began to stroke her cheek, her slender neck, and his arm came round her as if he could not help its movement. His fingers slid into the neck of her blouse, seeking her skin, and she closed her eyes and leaned forward when his hand brushed her breast and curled around it possessively.

'God, no!' He moved away, angry and impatient with himself, his hands thrust into his pockets. 'Now do you see why I'm going?' he asked harshly. 'While I'm anywhere near you I'll come for you.'

'You—you mean, it's all for my own good?' Tamara choked. 'I don't believe you! If you loved me you'd want to stay, want to be with me. You're saying this to excuse the other night, just as you pretended to want me when you were at my flat. Excuses! You didn't phone me. I just walked out of your house while you were still asleep, but you didn't phone, didn't wonder why. Stop lying to me! You were glad to see me go. It lets you off the hook.'

He turned eyes on her that were almost on fire but stopped his angry reply when he saw tears streaming down her cheeks.

'I thought you'd simply gone to work,' he explained tightly. 'I woke up and Claire was there, complaining, demanding. My head was killing me too. When you stayed with me my body wanted more than it was capable of accepting, and next morning I was paying for it. Claire said you'd gone to work and I was glad you wouldn't be there to hear the arguing. When I got rid of her and phoned the shop you'd left. You weren't at the flat and Janet only knew the name of this village. I searched for you, Tamara,' he ended wearily.

'If—if you searched for me...why did you bother?' she asked bitterly. 'Why didn't you just go away and forget it all? You don't trust me. You don't trust anyone.'

'I'll always hurt you, Tamara,' he said sombrely. 'Everything about me will hurt you. If I stay we'll go on being lovers and you know it. That's not for you, no life for you. I'm going.' He turned away and there was nothing she could do.

By the time they got back to the house Tamara was in control of her feelings, and it helped that she was numb with disbelief. She loved him. He said he loved her but he was ruthlessly cutting her out of his life. He was stiff with self-control, a tightness about his face that drew attention to him.

He politely thanked her mother and prepared to leave. Her mother coaxed but Jason refused to stay at all.

'Can't you stay all night?' Susan Rawson asked with a pleading smile. 'Tomorrow is our big day. It's Tamara's birthday.'

Jason looked at Tamara, and his lips twisted wryly when he saw hope in her face.

'I'm sorry. I can't,' he told her mother firmly. 'Tomorrow I have to settle all my affairs and then I'm leaving. I'll be in London for a few days and then I'm flying out to America. I have no idea when I'll be back.' He turned back to Tamara. 'Sign the lease, please,' he said in a very formal voice. 'I want it all settled before I go.'

'Yes. All the loose ends tied up!' she exclaimed with so much bitterness that her mother frowned anxiously and Rob's hand came to her shoulder. He didn't know what was happening, but he knew there was something and he was showing his support. She smiled at him bleakly, and when Jason silently handed her a pen she scribbled her name. She had no idea what it looked like. She didn't seem to know who she was any more.

Two weeks later Tamara stood in the shop and watched Mrs Prost leave with one of the season's most expensive suits.

'I won't say I told you so,' Janet murmured as the door closed. 'Notice the change of attitude?'

'Do you think we have the upper hand?' Tamara asked drily.

'Oh, I think so.' Janet smiled quite smugly. 'Two weeks and they're back. They've noted our superior attitude too. We'll not have any trouble in future.'

Tamara turned away. It was true that Janet had adopted an attitude that had impressed. She, however, had not needed to. She just wasn't interested any more. Life had almost stopped, and each day was a repetition of the next, everything mechanical.

Before she'd left home she had told her mother about Jason. In fact, she hadn't been able to avoid it because when he went she had broken down and shut herself away to weep. It was like some terrible misunderstanding. She couldn't take it in and she still couldn't. Inside she knew that if he really loved her he would be here now, wanting to be with her, but she hadn't seen him again.

She had stuck it out for a whole week and then she had driven past his house, behaving like a teenager, wanting to see the place where he would be. He was not there, though. Outside was an estate agent's board and she had driven away with the words ringing round in her head. For Sale. He had gone, just as he had said. He had cut her out of his life, tied up the loose ends.

Hope still clung and she had telephoned his office on Victoria Crescent, only to be told that Mr Tysak was in London for one day more and then he would be in America. He wasn't coming back. The business at this end was completed.

So it seemed, completed or abandoned. Nobody was working on the hotel, everything had settled into limbo and Tamara suspected he would finally sell everything and wipe out the time he had spent here altogether. He had wiped out his time with her and each day she tried to forget him and start again.

She was just finishing her supper when Roger called at the flat. Over the two weeks they had made up their differences. He had accepted that friendship was all he was going to get. After a long look at her he had stead-fastly refrained from mentioning Jason, and with his new attitude she had no hesitation about letting him in.

'I wasn't expecting visitors,' she told him ruefully, looking down at her dressing-gown. 'I'm having a lazy evening.'

'I'm not staying long.' Roger glanced keenly at her and closed the door. 'Let's have a cup of tea. I've got something to tell you. As a matter of fact, I need advice, somebody to bounce ideas off.'

'Maybe I'm not qualified to give advice,' Tamara muttered, leading the way into the kitchen to put the kettle on.

'I think you are. Your head is well screwed on.'

It almost made her laugh; in fact, she gave a small, bitter smile. Jason had once told her that her brain was only loosely attached to her body. He had said she was young, too young. She felt really old at the moment; worn out, even.

It was all explained as they drank their tea.

'I've been offered a job on a big London paper,' Roger informed her slowly. He glanced up and gave a wry look in her direction. 'Actually, I applied in a fit of temper, the night after the fashion show and our big row. I never thought about it being accepted. I went down for an interview last week.'

'And never told me?'

'I didn't quite believe it, as a matter of fact. Miracles don't often drift by.'

'So what's the problem? Will you be the editor?'

He threw his head back and laughed uproariously.

'No way, love! I'm a newsman from the backwoods. It's only because I'm the editor of the local rag that I've made it at all. The job is for features editor, taking over on a two-month basis.'

'Is that good?' Tamara asked ingenuously.

'It's good. Should I take it, though?' He looked at her steadily. 'If I thought for one moment that you——'

'I'm your friend, Roger. I'll always be that, but nothing more. If you want this job then go for it.'

'Tysak left, Tamara,' he said grimly.

'I know. He told me he was leaving. I don't expect to see him again.'

'The hotel is going ahead, and the work on Lancrest Mews. Did you know it?' he asked, looking at her worriedly.

'No, but I'm not surprised and I'm glad. It will be really good. I saw something like it when Jason and I went . . . went . . .'

'Oh, Tamara!' He took her hand but she gently extricated herself and stood, walking about, deliberately cheerful.

'It's all right. Let's talk about this job of yours.'

They talked for an hour, tossing things back and forth, the salary, which would be bigger, the expenses, which would be more, but there was a good future there and she knew that Roger needed to tie up loose ends too. She was nothing more than that to him if he would admit it. By the time he left he was convinced, and she felt satisfied that it was best for him.

Rob would have found it all amusing, she thought, glancing at herself in the mirror as she closed the door on Roger. Agony aunt. Rob would certainly have called her that. He was coming to see her in a couple of days and the idea brightened her up a little. She had walked over the hills with Rob and poured out her heart to him, wept on his shoulder.

The bell rang and she got up from her chair in the sitting-room, glancing round quickly. As far as she could see, Roger hadn't left anything behind. Maybe in the hall. She tried to remember what he had brought with him but there was only his coat; he'd taken that.

When she opened the door it was not Roger at all. Jason stood there, tall, dark, menacing and looking at her with blazing eyes. He just came right in, closing the door behind him, and she stepped back out of his way, unable to say a word.

'I can see that you're different,' he rasped, his eyes running over her. 'As I understand it, you never floated around in your robe when Hart was here. In fact, he rarely came here at all, according to you. Surely he just left? Here you are, though, ready for bed.'

He looked furious and Tamara could only stare at him with wide amber eyes. She clutched the edge of the table in the hall, not really able to believe he was here. When Jason said something he meant it, and he had left. Why was he back? To torment her? She couldn't speak and he came closer, towering over her.

'Is he coming here now? Are you back with him?'

'What do you want? Why are you here?' She just stared at him wildly, her face perfectly white.

'Answer my question! What was Hart doing here?'

'It comes under the heading of none of your business,' Tamara stated clearly. She had no idea why he was back but she was sensible enough to know that she had to defend herself. She would not allow this possessive demanding. 'You have no right to even come here, and certainly no right to ask questions about how I live my life. You're nothing to do with me at all, Jason.'

It wiped the fury off his face immediately and she turned away, her back to him. She was pretty annoyed herself because she couldn't even look at him without wanting to run right into his arms. He was here to start all the misery up again.

'I want to have the right,' he said in a desperate voice. 'These two weeks have been hell. I had to come back because I can't keep away and I'm never going to be able to keep away.'

Tamara turned slowly to look at him. It was a bit too early to let her guard down and she knew it. Anyone with any sense would keep him at arm's length, make him state his intentions quite clearly, but somehow she knew she would never have that sort of sense with Jason. He would always be the driving force in her life.

'I—I'm twenty-five now...' she began tremulously, looking at him with wide anxious eyes, and he reached for her blindly, his arms tightening round her to the point of pain.

'I don't care how old you are, who you are, what you are,' he admitted thickly. 'I just know that I love you and I can't walk out of your life. You're too much a part of mine.'

He swept her up into his arms and walked through to the sitting-room, holding her cradled against him, and Tamara clung to him tightly, hardly able to breathe, so much happiness welling up inside that she felt unable to speak. He sat down and held her on his knee, his hand sweeping back her hair and cupping her flushed face.

'Tammy, darling!' He began to kiss her, giving her no time to say anything at all, and her arms wound around his neck as she gave herself up to the sheer bliss of being back with him. 'I couldn't go,' he murmured against her lips. 'I had to come back to you. If you finally leave me it's a chance I'll have to take. I suppose everyone takes that chance when they get married.'

'Are you asking me to marry you?' Tamara wanted to know, great joy bubbling up inside.

'I'm telling you,' he assured her grimly. 'I won't take no for an answer either.'

She pulled back and smiled up into his face.

'You won't get no for an answer. I can't say that these two weeks have been anything but misery for me either.' Her slender fingers stroked the smooth rasp of his cheek. 'I'll never leave you, Jason. I'll be that immovable object always.'

He gave a shaken laugh and began to kiss the silken line of her throat.

'I've thought it all out,' he whispered. 'I'll have you so tied up in my life that getting free would be an impossibility. You'll have too many children; you'll be too busy.'

'I want children,' Tamara said dreamily, lying back in his arms. 'We'll be surrounded by love and warmth. You won't ever want to go to work.'

He slid down the zip of her robe and found the warm curve of her breast.

'Go on,' he urged huskily. 'I can listen to this all night.' But Tamara was soon too deeply committed to the moment to think of the future, and when he lifted her and carried her to the lamplit bedroom she melted into his arms, ready to give him all the love inside her.

'I could stand to hear three little words,' Jason murmured against her skin when at last their breathing returned to normal. 'You've promised a lot of things but never made any solid statement.' His head lifted and his dark eyes swept over her adoringly. 'Tell me, sweetheart, even if you only say it once in your life.'

'I'll never stop saying it,' Tamara cried, raining hot kisses against his face. 'I love you, Jason. I've fought you and raged at you but I suppose I've loved you from the moment I saw you.'

'I *wanted* you from the moment I saw you,' he confessed wryly, smiling down at her. 'When I kissed you out in the rain I started to get worried. You responded to me as if you belonged to me and that should have been a triumph, but every bit of caution in me said stop right there, she'll mean too much to you.' He laughed down at her. 'I'm not sure which one of us was the irresistible force, darling. Each time I put you out of my mind you were doing something to force yourself back in there again. When I saw you with Hart I was wild with rage, more wild because I knew then what it meant, and I was determined not to be trapped into anything. The fashion show was the last straw.'

'Why?' Tamara looked at him sideways, her tawny eyes smiling, and his face darkened with desire. He didn't answer until she had been kissed passionately and was once again subdued.

'I didn't want anyone else looking at you, for one thing,' he muttered. 'For another, I wanted all that subtle display of sex to be aimed at me only. I wanted you to mean it.'

'It was all tricks of the trade,' Tamara said teasingly, stretching like a cat beneath him until his body began to move restlessly over her. 'I'm too well brought up to behave like that in real life.'

'You're doing quite well now,' Jason growled, nipping her shoulder. 'Tammy, say you'll never leave me!'

'Never, ever,' she promised softly, her hands cupping his face. 'I've got a very stable home background. In our family we never divorce. My mother and father have been married for almost thirty years and Rob's parents have been married for thirty-three years. Now my Aunt Constance, that's on my mother's side, married when she was eighteen, and they're still happily married at fifty.' She looked up into his laughing face. 'Don't you like my family lectures?'

'I love them, darling. I'm dying to meet all these people.'

'Oh, you will,' Tamara said earnestly. 'We stick together. And, by the way, Robbie's coming in a couple of days—you can get to know him. He makes fabulous furniture. It would look super in any hotel.'

'Always the business lady,' Jason grinned, moving from the bed and beginning to dress. 'I distinctly heard you say that his furniture was all crafty woodwork.'

'Only to annoy him,' Tamara assured him seriously. 'We tease constantly. You'll see.'

'Where is he staying when he comes here?' Jason asked, pulling her from the bed and into his arms. 'We seem to have one bedroom and one bed. The settee is definitely out of bounds because I'll be here and I'll demand privacy.'

'Are you staying here?' Tamara asked with a coy look, and he kissed her hard.

'I sold my house. I'm homeless until we're married. We could move into a hotel and let Rob have this flat.'

'Rob uses the hotel,' Tamara assured him firmly. 'I'm a working girl.'

'For how long?' Jason asked as they ate supper together, sitting at the table in the kitchen and smiling into each other's eyes. 'I want you with me and I have to travel quite a lot. I hadn't even thought of buying a house here until I saw you. You didn't like it anyway, and neither did I. We could buy a place pretty close to your mother and father—if you want that?'

'Oh, Jason, I do!' Her hands reached out for him and he gathered them in his own. 'I want to draw you so closely into my life that you'll never even think of life without me.'

'I can't think of life without you now,' he said huskily. 'What about the shop, though?'

'Janet could run it,' she suggested. 'I could set up another place in Cumbria—and see to it when we're not travelling,' she added hastily when he gave her a ferocious frown.

'I can see we're about to expand into the glamour trade,' Jason murmured wryly. 'Impressions in every town and all my hotels filled with Rob's furniture.'

'It's not a bad idea,' Tamara said seriously, and Jason nodded thoughtfully.

'Just so that our house is filled with my children, starting very soon.'

'Geronimo,' Tamara muttered, blushing prettily.

'I never did find out why you said that when we first met,' he murmured in an intrigued voice as he stood and pulled her to her feet.

'I thought you were a noble savage,' Tamara said seriously, looking up at him. 'I felt like a demure maiden, ordained to serve you.'

'*You*?' He gave a great shout of laughter and swung her up into his arms. 'My beautiful darling, you lie as wonderfully as you do everything else. I'll spend the rest of my life watching my step and I know it.'

'Behind every powerful man is a good woman,' Tamara stated huffily.

'Trying to get two steps in front of him,' Jason grinned, holding her close. 'It doesn't matter, my love. All I care about is having you so tied down that you'll never wriggle free.'

'I'll never want to,' Tamara said softly as their lips met.

'I almost forgot,' Jason murmured as they sat side by side in the sitting-room later. 'You had a birthday.' He took a box from his pocket and slipped a glittering ring on to her finger as she watched, enchanted. 'Engaged!' he stated firmly. 'Mine!'

Tamara twisted her hand, watching the glitter of diamonds in the light.

'I suppose this is how you get to be really rich,' she sighed teasingly. 'A birthday and engagement rolled into one.'

'Well, I thought about it,' Jason laughed, 'but after due consideration I felt I could afford a present. How about these?' He presented her with earrings to match the ring, carefully fixing them and then sitting back to look at her adoringly. 'That just about covers everything,' he said softly. 'We planned the business venture and the house purchase.'

'So what's left?' Tamara asked, her cheeks flushing at the look in his eyes.

'The family,' he decided, reaching for her and pulling her close. 'We should get around to that at once, and no arguments.'

'Not one,' Tamara agreed, winding her arms around his neck.

Accept 4 FREE Romances and 2 FREE gifts

FROM READER SERVICE

n irresistible invitation from
ills & Boon Reader Service. Please
ccept our offer of 4 free Romances,
CUDDLY TEDDY and a special
YSTERY GIFT... Then, if you choose,
o on to enjoy 6 captivating
omances every month for just £1.70
ch, postage and packing free.
us our FREE Newsletter with author
ews, competitions and much more.

nd the coupon below to:
eader Service, FREEPOST,
O Box 236, Croydon,
urrey CR9 9EL.

NO STAMP REQUIRED

es! Please rush me 4 Free Romances and 2 free gifts!
ease also reserve me a Reader Service Subscription. If I decide to subscribe I
n look forward to receiving 6 brand new Romances each month for just
0.20, post and packing free.
I choose not to subscribe I shall write to you within 10 days - I can keep the
oks and gifts whatever I decide. I may cancel or suspend my subscription
any time. I am over 18 years of age.

s/Mrs/Miss/Mr ——————————————————— EP30R

ddress ————————————————————————

———————————————————————————————

ostcode——————————— Signature ———————————

Next Month's Romances

Each month you can choose from a wide variety of romance with Mills & Boon. Below are the new titles to look out for next month, why not ask either Mills & Boon Reader Service or your Newsagent to reserve you a copy of the titles you want to buy — just tick the titles you would like and either post to Reader Service or take it to any Newsagent and ask them to order your books.

Please save me the following titles:	Please tick	√
BACHELOR AT HEART	Roberta Leigh	
TIDEWATER SEDUCTION	Anne Mather	
SECRET ADMIRER	Susan Napier	
THE QUIET PROFESSOR	Betty Neels	
ONE-NIGHT STAND	Sandra Field	
THE BRUGES ENGAGEMENT	Madeleine Ker	
AND THEN CAME MORNING	Daphne Clair	
AFTER ALL THIS TIME	Vanessa Grant	
CONFRONTATION	Sarah Holland	
DANGEROUS INHERITANCE	Stephanie Howard	
A MAN FOR CHRISTMAS	Annabel Murray	
DESTINED TO LOVE	Jennifer Taylor	
AN IMAGE OF YOU	Liz Fielding	
TIDES OF PASSION	Sally Heywood	
DEVIL'S DREAM	Nicola West	
HERE COMES TROUBLE	Debbie Macomber	

If you would like to order these books in addition to your regular subscription from Mills & Boon Reader Service please send £1.70 per title to: Mills & Boon Reader Service, P.O. Box 236, Croydon, Surrey, CR9 3RU, quote your Subscriber No:..
(If applicable) and complete the name and address details below. Alternatively, these books are available from many local Newsagents including W.H.Smith, J.Menzies, Martins and other paperback stockists from 4th December 1992.

Name:..

Address:...

....Post Code:.........................

To Retailer: If you would like to stock M&B books please contact your regular book/magazine wholesaler for details.

You may be mailed with offers from other reputable companies as a result of this application.
If you would rather not take advantage of these opportunities please tick box ☐